Communication in the Animal World

Communication

in the Animal World

William F. Evans

Illustrated by Nancy Lou Gahan

Thomas Y. Crowell Company
New York   Established 1834

Designed by Barbara Kohn Isaac

Manufactured in the United States of America
L. C. Card 68-21612
1 2 3 4 5 6 7 8 9 10

For Annette and Donna

Foreword

This book has been written with the general reader, the student, and the scientist in mind. In summarizing the knowledge of any field of scientific endeavor, as has been attempted here, care must be taken to avoid becoming so absorbed in detail that not only the underlying causes and effects but the unifying explanations and reasons as well are obscured. Therefore, technical aspects of the study of animal communication have been kept to a minimum.

Animal communication is carried on in a surprisingly well-coordinated, predictable manner, and serves the useful purpose of integrating the innumerable functions—food gathering, defense, maintenance of territorial integrity, courtship and mating, and care of the young—of a biological population. The survival of that population (as well as of the individual animal) depends to a large extent on the effectiveness of its systems of communication.

Only recently have we begun to understand a few of the complicated mechanisms involved in the social behavior of animals and to realize more fully the significance of the numerous methods whereby various species of animals convey information—possibly even ideas—to one another. Our ignorance is still quite overwhelming. In higher mammals, for instance, we do not know the roles played by instinct and learning in the development of "languages." We have only the vaguest notion concerning the extent to which these typically stereotyped communicatory patterns can be modified if the need arises—that is, what degree of adaptability the particular animal possesses in this respect.

In this introduction to the subject of animal communication, not all the possible channels for signal transfer have been explored. Heat-sensitive organs and the controversial phenomenon known as extrasensory perception, for example, purposely have been omitted, although there is evidence that both these and other channels and mechanisms may function in a communicative manner. Our purpose has been not to present an elaborate dissertation but to define and delimit our subject to some degree.

Only a few of the many thousands of different kinds of animals will be considered in this book, and only a handful of those under consideration will be discussed at length. The reason for this is that the bulk of the research—and therefore of the knowledge we now have—regarding signaling in animals revolves around these few.

Every author depends a great deal upon the generosity of others. I should like to take this opportunity to thank Doctors James H. Fribourgh and Clarence B. Sinclair for their patience and helpful suggestions during preparation of the manuscript; Dr. George B. Schaller, who so kindly permitted me to use some of his descriptions of gorilla vocalizations; the Kay Electric Company for supplying technical data regarding the sound spectrograph; and my colleagues and students at Little Rock University, who have continually offered encouragement and inspiration. A very special note of thanks is due the publisher, at whose suggestion this book has been written, and Mary B. Irving for editorial assistance.

WILLIAM F. EVANS

Contents

1. Introduction   1

2. Aquatic Invertebrates and Fishes   13

3. Insects   29

4. Reptiles and Amphibians   55

5. Birds   73

6. Land Mammals   95

7. Aquatic Mammals   119

8. Primates   135

9. Methods and Tools for Study   161

   Selected Bibliography   172

   Index   177

Illustrations

Photographs

Large claw of the male fiddler crab   15
Rock barnacle with feet extended   17
Head of a sea bass   20
Swarm of bees   33
Worker bee feeding a queen larva   40
Ants exchanging food   44
Harvester ants following scent trail   45
Western diamondback rattlesnake   57
Cobra snake in defense position   58
Front view of a toad   71
Young loggerhead shrikes   74
Flock of birds   82
Eastern robin feeding its young   85
Two bull elk fighting over herd of cows   100
Two zebras nuzzling   102
Seal rookery on St. Paul Island in Bering Sea   109
Bottle-nosed dolphins   127
Adult gorilla engaged in chest-slapping display   142
Chimpanzee adult and young   158
Robert C. Hermes photographing birds   166

Drawings

Toad and millipede   5
Copulating snails   7
Male and female sticklebacks   23
Hermaphroditic groupers   24
Scallops and starfish   26
Stag beetles   31
Immature grasshopper   35
Silkworm moths   50
Rattlesnake dance   60
Copulating geckos   61
Frilled lizard   62
Alligator snapping turtle   63
Saw-whet owl and mouse   76
Herring gull   83
Albatrosses dancing   90
Bird of paradise   92
Buck hares fighting   101
Young Arab stallions fighting   105
Opossum playing dead   107
Mother dolphin feeding young   122
Nocturnal angwantibo   137
Hamadryad baboon   147
Baboon mother and babies   150
Chimpanzees hunting termites   154
Recording hummingbird sounds   164

The wild gander leads his flock through the cool night,
Ya-honk he says, and sounds it down to me like an
  invitation,
The pert may suppose it meaningless, but I listening
  close,
Find its purpose and place up there toward the wintry
  sky.

"Song of Myself"
WALT WHITMAN

1. Introduction

All animals must solve the basic problems of food and reproduction if they are to survive. Their continued attempts to do so successfully in a continually changing environment have resulted in the amazing variety of animal life in the world today. There are, for example, perhaps 1,150,000 species— among them about 900,000 species of insects, to which some 5,000 new species are added every year. Some species are so tiny that they are invisible to the naked eye. Some travel vast distances to nesting grounds; the arctic tern, for instance, makes a round trip of up to 22,000 miles each year between the Arctic and Antarctic. And each species has its natural enemies. Numbers, size, space, predation—all are obstacles to be overcome if an animal is to succeed in finding the right food supply, in locating and identifying the right mate, in fending off competition and danger. In a vast, hostile world there can be no room for error in the information received or transmitted that relates to these basic necessities, if the animal is to survive. This is the unique purpose for which animal communication systems and mechanisms have been designed.

What Is Communication?

Communication involves the production of a signal, by an individual or a group, which stimulates a response in a receiver. In general our discussion assumes sender and receiver to be of the same species. The sensory stimulus comprising the signal may consist, for example, of a sound or series of sounds arranged in a definite sequence or pattern; a display of gestures, facial expressions, body positions, and coloration; an emission of odors; or actual physical contact. The signal is mediated (that is, transmitted from sender to receiver) through the air or through water as sound, smell, touch, taste, or as a visual stimulus; or through the ground, fallen logs, or other substrate as vibrations. When received through the sensory organs of the receiver, the signal causes changes in the receiver's internal condition, influencing its external behavior. The response of an animal to a communicatory signal is not always obvious; in fact, the very act of ignoring a signal may constitute a proper response, as when a dominant ape ignores a subordinate ape, the first animal thus indicating that he is still in command.

The physical senses of sight, sound, and touch, and the chemical senses of smell and taste all play important roles in animal communication. In most animals the chemical senses are well developed and are the most widely used in communication. The visual and auditory senses become the most important communicatory channels in those animals with highly developed sight and hearing. Visual and auditory signals can relay more information with greater precision than can other types of signals. But hearing is not so important for the survival of animals as are the senses of sight, smell, and touch.

Certain advantages and disadvantages are inherent in any kind of signal. An odor, for example, is highly specific and often persistent and effective over long distances. But odors are frequently dispersed by wind, washed away by rain, or masked by competing odors in the environment. Also, scents are usually poor indicators of direction.

Signals depending upon vision are highly directional in nature and very effective at short range; but darkness, thick foliage, muddy water, vulnerability of the signaler to predation, and other conditions tend to limit the usefulness of visual signals in communication. Touch, with no exceptions, and taste, with a few, require that two parties be in physical contact in order for a transfer of information to take place. Communication through these senses, therefore, is little affected by the environment. Although widely used by higher mammals, birds, insects, and a few other animals, auditory signals are affected by wind, density of foliage, thunderstorms, and interfering noises generally.

Some animals use compound signals involving several sensory stimuli in carrying out the often vital process of transmitting and receiving information. Exploitation of multiple signals makes possible a more complex and extensive vocabulary of signals, such as that occurring among the primates.

Communication Mechanisms and Structures

Animals receive information about their environment through their sense organs, which receive and relay stimuli to a central nervous system. The degree to which animals are able to exploit communication systems depends upon the level of development of their sensory and nervous systems. The reactions of an animal with poor eyesight, for example, are restricted chiefly to nonvisual elements in the environment.

Sense organs increase in complexity from the lower to the higher animals, and the latter have intricate, specialized structures for sight, hearing, touch, taste, and smell. Insects, for example, have eyes with fixed lenses that cannot focus but are excellent for detecting motion; the vertebrate eye, on the other hand, forms clear, focused images.

Within the animal kingdom a wide variety of organs exist for the production or perception of sounds. Man and other mammals have vocal folds, or "cords," inside a special organ, the larynx. Birds have a syrinx, or sound box, at the base of the windpipe. But not all sounds produced by animals are vocalizations. The rasping stridulation of insects, the "drumming" of certain fishes, and the chest slapping of gorillas are highly effective as communicatory signals. Some animals are especially sensitive to vibrations that reach them through the ground. Sound vibrations travel in all directions from their source in the form of waves. The number of sound waves that occur per second is referred to as the frequency, or pitch, of the sound. Frequency is usually measured in cycles per "kilo-ond; when the frequency is extremely high, the term "kilo-cycle," meaning 1,000 cycles, is often used.

The human ear can detect sound vibrations occurring within the relatively narrow frequency range of approximately 20 to 20,000 cycles per second. Certain insects, bats, aquatic mammals, and other animals produce vibrations beyond the range of human hearing. Those too high for the unaided human ear to detect are said to be ultrasonic; those falling below the range of unaided audibility are subsonic. Both ultrasonic and subsonic frequencies can be readily detected by the use of modern electronic apparatus.

Frequency, amplitude (loudness), and duration (time) are among the most important qualities of sound where animal communication is concerned. Often, for instance, the suitor making the loudest noise frightens away an enemy or wins a mate during courtship. Other qualities of sound, such as rhythm and pulsation, are also important.

Although we associate scent with our noses, and taste with our mouths and tongues, some animals (many insects, for example) have taste organs in their feet and scent organs in their antennae. The hairs of insects also are often used for the sense of touch. Compared with the organs for seeing and hearing, those dealing with the sense of touch in most animals are simple. Each tactile organ consists of a nerve ending enveloped by layers of tissue; separate groups of nerve cells receive the sensations of pain, cold, heat, touch, and pressure.

All the sense organs pass their information to the brain. Increased brain size is one of the characteristics of mammals. The cerebellum, controlling coordination and balance, and the cerebrum, controlling memory, the senses, and voluntary action, make up most of the mammalian brain's total volume. In the higher mammals cerebral furrows greatly increase the brain's total surface area. The brain's gray matter (the cerebral cortex, or outer surface) is most complex in the primates; here are located the nerve endings for intelligence or learning.

Most millipedes can spray noxious or poisonous fumes at any predator that tries to eat them. This unfortunate toad has just spat out a millipede that sprayed the toad's mouth and tongue with a liquid containing deadly hydrogen cyanide gas. Most wild animals learn to avoid millipedes and will reject them in laboratory tests.

Uses of Communication

Animals live in a complex biological environment, in which they must be assured of a place where they can feed and breed in safety. Unless animals compete directly for the same item of food at the same time, they tend to ignore each other. As a general rule, territories of species with the same food preferences do not overlap, with the result that animals are spaced out fairly evenly over a whole area.

Many animals live in groups, or aggregations; and the maintenance of the intact group is often dependent upon the effectiveness of its system of identifying members of the same group. This is also true in the case of animals that maintain individual home territories.

Aggressive display, ritualized fighting, and territorial behavior are all related to species recognition. Each animal marks out the boundaries of its home territory, which it then proceeds to defend against any intruder of the same species, whether it be a potential rival for a mate or a threat to the "home." Sometimes a territory is held by an individual, sometimes by a group or colony. Territorial size varies: mammals have smaller territories than birds because they see much less on the ground and cannot get around so quickly. The territory usually is maintained inviolate only within the species.

Aggression to seize territory is rare in the animal world. Because most animals appear to have an instinctive respect for another's territory, the territorial signal or defense threat often is sufficient to halt an intruder. If it does not, and the intruder chooses to fight, he generally loses. This may be because the intruder never reacts as strongly to threats as the owner of the territory does. Outside its own territory an animal seems to be at a disadvantage.

Signals that aid in social cooperation are alarm, warning, distress, and food calls, as well as those calls that help to maintain a dominance hierarchy or social caste system, as found in many birds and primates.

Attracting a mate is the first step in the reproduction

process. The mating call of the bull moose is a case in point. Male and female might find each other by pure chance, but the bellowing vocalizations of the bull help to assure the attraction of one or more mates and, incidentally, warn other bulls away. When male and female have come together, final identification and often elaborate courtship rituals—as in birds, for example—are necessary to arouse the mating instinct. Unlike that of birds, courtship among mammals usually is relatively simple, since male and female must both be in the right physiological state at the same time to mate successfully.

Where the young are left to develop on their own, there is no development of communicatory patterns between them and their parents. But where the behavior patterns of the young are acquired chiefly through experience, complex com-

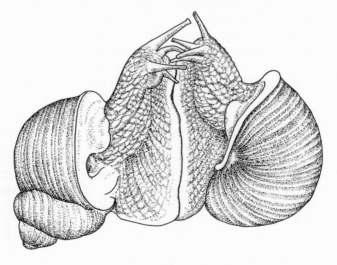

The end purpose of most animal communication within any one species is reproduction. Among land snails touch appears to be the key sense individuals use to show that they are ready to mate. Courtship starts when two of these creatures brush mouths and feelers against each other. Then for a while they move about in a slow dance. Finally, after spending several hours pressed sole to sole, these bisexual land molluscs exchange sperm to fertilize each other's eggs.

munication systems may develop, changing as the young mature. Among mammals, for example, the period of parental care and supervision ranges from a few weeks to several years, while the young learn to seek food and to defend themselves.

Certain patterns of behavior, such as nest building and courtship, are instinctive and do not have to be learned. But if an animal is to acquire the new behavior needed to adjust to new situations arising in its environment, it can do so only by learning. The chief way that animals learn new behavior is by imitating the learned behavior of older, more experienced members of the species.

The ability to use communicative signs symbolically—to pass on from generation to generation information regarding the history and culture of a species, and to discuss the present and the future—has long been attributed to man alone. Dedicated researchers now believe, however, that certain aquatic mammals (notably dolphins, porpoises, and whales) may have true languages that compare favorably with, and in some cases may even surpass, the languages of man.

Can Animals Speak Languages?

Although communication is an essential part of the social life of animals, their "languages" are built upon entirely different principles from ours. For that reason efforts to establish interspecific communication with various animals have not achieved spectacular success. In their book *The Ape in Our House*, Cathy and Keith Hayes point out that after raising a chimpanzee, Vicki, in their home as though it were a child, the ape was able to learn only four words: "mama," "papa," "cup," and "up." The learned words were uttered parrotlike, without variable inflection.

In a valiant attempt to teach a monkey to vocalize, Dr. John Lilly placed electrodes in the brain of the unanesthetized simian so that an electrical stimulus passed through the electrodes induced sensations of pleasure. The monkey quickly learned to push the button that operated the stimulus, using it over and over again for hours on end. But when the button was moved away from the restrained animal, he could not be taught to vocalize in order to receive the pleasure stimulus as a reward. Time and time again he seemed on the verge of making sounds, but apparently he could not associate vocalization with the reward. A total of three monkeys was used during a series of these tests. But after six months and hundreds of trials the researchers concluded that the association would never be made.

Nevertheless, there are highly competent and respected scientists who feel that communication with an animal is not only possible but may come about within the next two decades. Dr. Lilly feels that this is true of dolphins, and others express the same idea in regard to the blue whale. Both these animals are cetaceans. They seem to be the only creatures with brains large and complex enough to make them potentially capable of understanding and being able to speak a human language. However, their vocal equipment may prove unsuitable. If these animals are found to possess a truly elaborate language—one that is capable of expressing more than the basic emotions of hunger, fear, anger, and so on—communication will have to be conducted electronically. Perhaps a goodly portion of this language will be in the form of ultrasonic sounds. If this is true, instruments may have to be used to lower the animal's "voice" to a range within our own audibility limits.

In one way at least, man can influence animals to modify the sounds they make so that, within limits, they approach those made by human beings. Just as human children must be in contact with human speech in order to develop the ability to speak a language, so a dolphin or other test animal must be closely associated with humans if it is to learn anything of human language. Also, if the test animal must listen to human words, or must itself vocalize before its basic needs are satisfied, it may be motivated to imitate the sounds of a human language more quickly.

As far as we know, only simple information is communicated by animals, virtually all of it concerned with carrying on the essential life processes. Animal communication deals with the immediate wants and fears of the present and does not tell of the past or of the future. Man seems to be the only animal with the ability to speak a true language; no animal lower on the evolutionary scale has ever been taught to speak or comprehend more than the most elementary words of a true language.

What Can We Learn from Animal Communication?

Chatting with whales and teaching dolphins Basic English to enable them to relay information about the measurement of sea temperatures, or the locations of rocket nose cones, are possible achievements that may ultimately spin off from studies in animal communication; but such activities constitute by no means the prime purpose of these studies. Of far greater interest and value to scientists—biologists, physiologists, psychologists, cyberneticists, electronic and computer experts, and so on—are the extension of knowledge and practical applications in the areas of animal behavior, human communication, agriculture, and wildlife management. Such new fields as bionics (application of the principles of living sensory systems to nonliving sensory systems), biosemiotics (the study of gestures, facial expressions, postures, and other visual signals), and pheromonics (the study of chemical signals) may also benefit from this research.

Because communication is a complex and integral part of animal behavior, a better understanding of the one is acquired through study of the other. Another by-product of investigations in the field of animal communication is an increased knowledge and understanding of the biological origins of human languages. It appears that linguistic ability, as well as the development of today's 3,000 different tongues, came about through the incredibly slow process of evolution.

The use of communication signals to influence the behavior of domestic animals—cattle, chicken, and even bees—has been practiced to a considerable extent in the field of agriculture.

In wildlife management, man has exercised his ability to mimic auditory and visual signals of birds and mammals. To lure a bull moose within shooting range, for example, hunters use a roll of birch bark shaped like a megaphone to imitate the guttural grunt of a challenging male or the moo of a love-sick cow. Decoys are employed to attract ducks to a blind during the hunting season, and the musky scent from musk-rat and beaver is used by trappers to attract other furbearers into their traps.

Pest control is another area where knowledge of animal communication systems is being put to good use. Tape-recorded acoustical alarm, assembly, and food calls have been broadcast over loudspeakers to repel or to attract birds, such as crows, starlings, gulls, and blackbirds, that may be inter-fering with the public peace or safety. It is possible that the use of ultrasonic signals to control rodents, such as rats and mice, may also prove effective.

To lure two insect pests—the black carpet beetle and the pine bark beetle—to their doom, Stanford Research Institute scientists are synthesizing the insects' own sex attractant. The attractant will be used to lure male beetles into traps, where they can be killed, or sterilized by radiation and then released to mate unfruitfully with females. Scientists from Stanford and the Southern Forest Experimental Station (in Louisiana) are also studying the trail-marking substance of the town ant, a species of leaf cutter that has infested shade and pine trees in Louisiana, Texas, and Mexico. When the substance is syn-thesized, it will be used to lure the insects into traps, where they can be killed. Such biological measures are highly selec-tive and present no danger to wildlife or man.

Studies of the vibration-sensitive "ear" on the foreleg of the long-horned grasshopper have been applied in improving the familiar microphone. Underwater detection and other problems related to antisubmarine warfare are being sur-mounted through the U. S. Navy's investigations into the sound-sensing capabilities of dolphins and whales and of the electric receptors of such fish as *Gymnarchus*. The commer-cial possibilities of bioluminescent cold light, emitted by fireflies and certain fish, have also been a subject of investigation in pheromonics research.

The first benefit to be derived from a study of animal communication is knowledge for its own sake. But many other far-reaching benefits result that affect and even influence a continually expanding range of human activities.

2. Aquatic Invertebrates and Fishes

Poets may rhapsodize about the "silence of the deep," but the sea in reality is a pretty noisy place. Many of the sounds of the sea are produced by its fishes and invertebrates. Toadfish toot like passing ships; marine catfish bark like seals; croakers and grunts, when caught, do what their names imply; and spiny lobsters squeak like creaky gates.

Dr. William N. Tavolga, a research associate at the American Museum of Natural History and a pioneer in the science of marine bioacoustics (the study of sound production and hearing among aquatic animals), says that the surface of the water reflects 99.9 percent of the sound that reaches it, giving the sea its illusion of quiet. Below the surface, however, the situation is quite different; for sounds carry better in water than in air. The sound produced by the explosion of less than half a dozen pounds of TNT, detonated a few thousand feet below the ocean's surface, can be identified 10,000 miles away with the aid of instruments.

Aquatic Invertebrates

Visual and auditory signals comprise the major part of the invertebrates' communicatory patterns. These animals without backbones, numbering about 800,000 known species, include such widely diversified forms of life as protozoans, worms, mollusks (such as clams, snails, and squid) and crustaceans (such as crabs, crayfish, and lobsters). These are not animals that we generally think of as communicating to any degree, if at all; yet communicate they must, if they are to survive.

Auditory Signals

Many crustaceans have special organs to produce sounds that are used as territorial markers and perhaps in mating as well. Spiny or rock lobsters (called crawfish in Florida) generate a scratching sound by rubbing the base of the antennae against the hard shell encasing their bodies. Certain crabs send their companions in hiding by vibrating a claw so that one or more of the joints rattle loudly. Male crabs often give this warning when a predator or human intruder approaches. For a considerable time during World War II, "whacking" noises as loud as those produced by a good-sized firecracker mystified submarine detection teams; the noise maker turned out to be the large claw of the snapping shrimp.

Clams and other bivalves make noises by repeatedly opening and closing their shells—the closing being performed with greater vigor. Barnacles also make noises in this fashion. Because of the great sound-transmitting capacity of water, barnacle snaps can be detected over long distances. Underwater microphones have picked up these sounds as far away as ten miles from the source.

Visual Signals

The eyesight of crustaceans is relatively well developed, so that visual signals are important in their communication. Like insects and certain other animals, crabs and lobsters have compound eyes—that is, eyes made up of thousands of smaller "eyes" called ommatidia. Each "eye," or ommatidium, operates like the individual cell of the retina of a vertebrate eye; thus the total image is built up of a series of spots.

Male crabs often develop brightly colored claws, which are used in attracting a mate and also in warning rival males. The large claw of the male fiddler crab is its badge of dominance. If the claw is removed or lost accidentally, the crab loses social position and is dominated by all the other crabs, with the exception of those that have also lost their large claw.

In the familiar courtship dance the crab may move the large claw sideways or in a vertical direction. Each species of crab can be distinguished by the rhythm and movement of this appendage. Sometimes the male "bows" when courting, and the female may approach and touch the suitor lightly and repeatedly with the antennae. She may then follow the male to

American Museum of Natural History

The large claw of the male fiddler crab not only plays an important part in the courtship ritual but helps establish the crab's social position as well. It can be waved horizontally or vertically as part of the courtship dance to entice a female, or moved in a threatening manner to warn off rivals. If the crab loses this oversized claw, he also loses his standing among the other crabs.

his burrow. At times she may move part way into a burrow and leave the legs on one side of her body protruding as a "keep out" signal.

Aggregations of feeding crabs probably make use of visual or tactile signals or both. As they prepare to forage, only a few individuals are seen to be moving. Soon, however, these are joined by others; all then move along in single file, with up to perhaps two dozen in a group.

Many of the deepwater marine invertebrates have photophores, or light-producing organs, which flash in rhythms characteristic of the particular species. One marine worm, known by its generic name *Odontosyllis*, is a good example. Only the male does the flashing; the female glows. At certain times of the year aggregations of females can be seen as a large glowing ball near the surface of the sea. The males start flashing and head for the females. If the latter dim their lights too quickly, the males halt and begin a series of bright, rapid flashes. The females respond and again light up.

Certain marine forms, such as shrimp and clams, often glow because they are infested with glowing parasitic bacteria, not because they have the power to light up. In this instance the light is continuous, never intermittent or flashing.

Chemical Signals

Aquatic invertebrates have no special taste or scent organs but are generally sensitive to chemicals over the entire body. The sense of taste, however, is important to lobsters and crabs, whose taste buds, resembling tiny hairs, are located on the feet.

Among the simplest forms of life, most of the signals employed are probably of a chemical nature. During the adult phase of its life cycle a multinucleate sheet of protoplasm known as a slime mold can be found moving across the ground, feeding upon decaying vegetation and live fungi. Some biologists class the slime molds as plants, others as animals, and still others as mixtures of the two. Perhaps it would be best to place them in a third kingdom, *Protista*. The slime molds begin as tiny bits of protoplasm, each with a single nucleus. Suddenly one of the cells begins to emit a chemical, acrasin, in rhythmic puffs. The rhythmic pattern of puffing seems to serve as an attractant, causing several of the single-celled organisms to aggregate and fuse into one mass so that reproduction can occur.

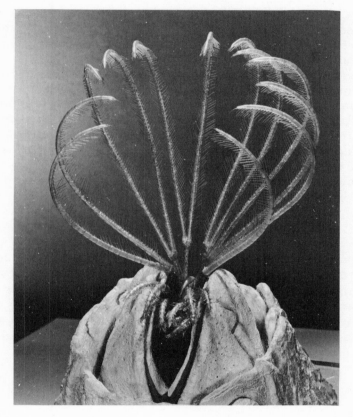

American Museum of Natural History
This common rock barnacle is shown with its feathery feet extended. These feet are primarily used for gathering food. The stationary adult barnacle sends out a chemical to attract barnacle larvae, which are able to swim freely.

Vorticella is a stalked protozoan that has tiny, hairlike projections called cilia around its upper end. The organisms are attached to twigs or small aquatic plants beneath the surface of freshwater ponds and streams. When the time for reproduction arrives, some of these one-celled animals send out a chemical attractant. Others of the genus have broken their stalks and, swimming with their cilia, move to the sessile forms so that conjugation can take place. Adult barnacles, like some of the individuals of *Vorticella*, remain attached. They send out a chemical attractive to barnacle larvae, which are motile.

Helix pomatia, a European land snail, exhibits an interesting interaction of chemical communication signals prior to mating. After exchanging an identifying "kiss" with another member of the species, one snail fires a so-called "love dart" into the other. The love dart, a small, arrowlike projectile, is produced from a special dart sac. Its excitatory effect is to make the recipient ready for the transfer of sperm. When this has been accomplished, the roles are reversed, and the first snail becomes the recipient of a love dart.

Tactile Signals

Coelenterates, the lowest forms of animal life to have cells differentiated into tissues, can communicate by means of tactile signals. Many of these minute aquatic animals live together in groups, or colonies. If even one member of the colony is lightly touched, it contracts into a tiny wad, and this action is quickly imitated by every other individual in the colony.

Fishes

Fishes use many types of communicatory signals, often in combination. For example, both chemical and visual signals are employed for identification; combined auditory and visual signals can be observed in courtship. All these signals, however, are somewhat specialized for operation in an aquatic environment.

Auditory Signals

I still recall vividly the first time I heard a freshwater drumfish sound off from a cypress-studded lake in the Deep South. The gathering darkness of a hot summer dusk, the trees with their grotesque aerating "knees" pointing skyward, and the eerie hooting of an owl mingling with the rolling, thumping beat of the drumfish were more than enough to excite the imagination of a small boy.

Fishes use sounds as mating calls, as schooling calls, as calls of species recognition and individual recognition, and as territorial defense signals. Male codfish grunt and display their fins to defend their spawning area and to induce the females to lay their eggs. Even freshwater minnows make thumping sounds that serve to attract females and to maintain a territory.

Salmon, bass, catfish, mackerel, and other teleosts (bony fishes) are much greater noise makers than are the nonbony fishes; and it appears that each family has its own distinctive sound-making mechanism.

The sound the sea bass makes when communicating with its mates originates from the beating of the opercula, or gill covers, against the sides of the head and chest region. Some members of this family produce sounds in rhythmical configurations of perhaps four or five sounds each. I have noticed this pattern in listening to recordings of the sounds made by a black grouper. The grouper, incidentally, produces these sounds in captivity if touched with a stick or other hard object or if placed in an aquarium with another species, such as a catfish. If the catfish comes near the grouper, the latter immediately begins a vigorous drumming sound—and the catfish hurriedly moves away.

In contrast to the sea bass, the toadfish has a swim, or air, bladder that actually produces sound rather than merely serving as a resonator. This organ has muscles and nerves of its own and—among certain species of toadfish found along the Atlantic coast, for example—is capable of producing grunting sounds. A Gulf of Mexico species is capable of making a powerful hooting sound, often described as resembling a boat whistle. This sound can be heard out of water without the aid of microphones, amplifiers, and such. It probably is involved in courtship, for both males and females have the same type of sound-making mechanism, and most of the hooting occurs at night. Some biologists think that the sound also is used as a means of keeping members of the same species together, especially at night or in turbid or murky waters during the day.

American Museum of Natural History
The head of a sea bass, showing the opercula, or gill covers. The sea bass communicates with his mate by rhythmically beating the opercula against the head or chest region.

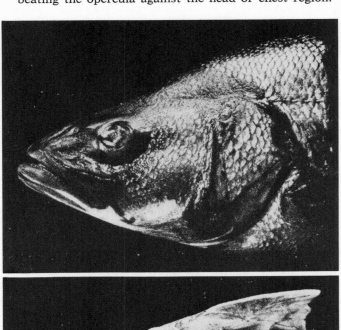

Gobies, blennies, and certain other families of bony fishes use sound to a great extent as a medium of communication; yet no sound-producing mechanism has been discovered in these groups, and the exact method of sound making is not known. Many of the thumping noises produced by the males during courtship are within the range of human hearing and have been recorded. These fishes often add emphasis by synchronizing their thumping with sharp, sideways snaps of the head. Possibly the head shaking and snapping set up a shock wave, which sounds like a thump when recorded. Sound making is restricted to the male goby and blenny and occurs only in the courting process. Violent body movements and color changes also occur at this time.

Fishes do not have external ears or eardrums like ours, and they do not hear as we do. Through tiny ear bones, called Weberian ossicles, sounds are conveyed to the nerves of the inner ear. In some of the bony fishes the ear bones are connected to the swim bladder, which serves as a resonator to amplify waterborne vibrations.

Various studies have revealed that although their inner ear has no cochlea (the device that permits mammals and birds to distinguish variations in pitch), fishes can distinguish both pitch and intensity of sound. Their range of pitch is more limited than man's, however: most fish are deaf to anything above high C, and hear best below middle A.

Many underwater animals can detect water motion and pressure changes that we cannot feel. A lateral line running along each side of its body permits the fish to sense water vibrations caused by other fish or nearby objects. Through small openings at the skin surface, water enters a collection of tubes running just beneath the surface of the skin. The movement of the water stimulates groups of hairs in the tubes which send impulses to the central nervous system. Fishes use this sensory system as an aid in seeking food or navigating in murky waters, in schooling with other fish or escaping enemies, or in courtship (swordtails, for example), where water is purposely pushed by one fish against another.

Another detecting device is the electrical field that electric eels set up around their bodies. Although completely blind, these fishes can sense the size, shape, and location of their fellows and of all other objects within twenty feet.

The soft-finned *Gymnarchus niloticus* of Africa has amazing sound-sensing capabilities. This fish emits low-voltage pulses ranging from 50 to 1,600 cycles per second and, by means of electrical receptors that serve as a kind of low-frequency radar, is able to detect changes in the pattern of the electrical field created by other fish or objects in surrounding waters. Specimens in an aquarium will respond to an electrostatic charge created by waving a comb that has been run through one's hair outside the aquarium. "These fish are sensitive to change in electrical field of the water of three billionths of a volt per millimeter," notes research chemist Donald E. Carr, "—a fantastically minute alteration very difficult to detect by even the most sensitive man-made instruments."

Visual Signals

Fishes have well-developed eyes that are similar in function, for the most part, to those of terrestrial animals. The eyes of fishes that inhabit the darker reaches of the ocean often are greatly reduced in size. Vision is limited to close-range use, such as distinguishing the patterns of other fish for identification. The marble-round shape of the eye lens is well suited to underwater vision. This shape gives the fish a far wider lateral field of vision than ours; but because there is little overlap of the visual fields in a forward direction, vision is almost entirely monocular—that is, each eye must focus separately on an object. Location of the eyes on the sides of the head rather than the front enables a fish to see far to the rear, in a direction almost parallel to the sides of the body.

Visual elements of the courting language play an important part in fish communication. A female goby will approach the recorded sound of a male goby, for instance, only when a male is actually placed in the aquarium with her. Sometime size alone serves as a warning signal between fish. A big bass warns others to keep away from its brood by virtue of its size, together with a few aggressive dartings toward the intruder.

Fishes do not stay in schools primarily for purposes of reproduction but because they see other fish. A totally blind fish will not school; a fish blind in one eye will line up with other fish on its seeing side.

Almost all fishes are known to have color vision, at least to some degree (sharks being the lone exception). Color is used in species identification and during courtship, or as a warning to predators that the fish is inedible or may fight if attacked. The spots and bizarre patterns and designs of many fishes also serve as courting and protective mechanisms. Sight is essential in bringing about a color change: blind fish cannot

After he has built a nest, the male stickleback gets the egg-laden female to enter it by dancing about and then nipping at her fins and tail.

change their coloration to match that of their environment and so obtain a protective camouflage.

The males of many fishes resemble birds in that they are much more brilliantly colored than the females. Colors show through the scales of those fishes that have scales; the pigments that form the colors reside in special color cells—the chromatophores—found in the skin. The presence of some colors is due to body wastes that lodge in the skin. The irridescent quality of fishes' skin is caused by the presence of a chemical known as guanin.

Mating colors in some species of fishes, for example, the male cuckoo wrasse, usually appear for only a few weeks and are entirely different from those seen at other times of the year. During spawning, the male cuckoo wrasse first scoops

Hermaphroditic groupers switch easily between male and female roles. When acting as a male, this fish has dark vertical stripes; in the female role it is unbanded. During the mating season a grouper will pair with a fish of the opposite pattern; the two chase and circle each other until, with a snap, they release eggs and sperm into the water. Then they can reverse roles—sometimes in as little as a few seconds.

out a crude nest in sand, then induces a female to lay her eggs in the nest by displaying his colors and by harassing her with nudges and nibbles.

Some fishes change color when they are angry or frightened. The color becomes paler if the fish is frightened, and deeper if an enemy is sighted. When the male cichlid, an African fish, takes over a territory on the sea bottom at mating time, he turns a bright red. When disturbed by a rival, he turns an even brighter red and spreads his dorsal fins to make himself look larger and more ferocious.

The colors of some fishes, such as *Betta splendens*, the Siamese fighting fish, show up when a mirror is placed so that the fish can see himself. There is the same display of aggression as when the fish actually sees another member of the same species. When a male *Betta* challenges an opponent, his color becomes more vivid, his fins spread, and his gill covers swing out to reveal brilliant red borders. The two fish proceed to swim along side by side. The pelvic fin closer to the other male is held stiffly down; the other pelvic fin is held against the body or is opened and closed like a pair of scissors. Suddenly one fish turns his head and stares at the other, who turns slightly away. The first fish straightens his head, and it is the other's turn to stare. This "if looks could kill" routine is repeated as the rivals continue to swim side by side. Occasionally one thrashes his tail in a wide sweep, sending wave currents to the other, who may reply in kind. Sometimes during this tail swinging, the fish may "stand" straight up on their tails.

In this display of aggression, each male is testing his opponent to make clear which one is the stronger. Eventually one male swims away, leaving the best spawning place to the stronger rival. If the fish are in an aquarium, actual combat will ensue and, unless removed from the tank, the loser will be killed.

Like the squid, shrimp, rays, and other denizens of the deep, fish with photophores generate light within specialized tissues. In fact, luminous marine animal species far outnumber the nonluminous species. None, however, is found below a depth of three miles. Some of the photophore cells and cell complexes in the light-emitting areas of the skin function as lamps, others as lenses, and still others as reflectors (as in the little lantern fish and hatchet fish)—beaming the light outward and downward so that it surrounds the fish in a protective cover. When viewed from below, the fish is lost in a luminous haze near the light surface of the water.

Chemical and Tactile Signals

Fishes have body patterns that can be used for identification, and they produce chemicals that can be used in the same way. Fishes of the same region have the same odor; in some species,

The most deadly enemy of the adult scallop is the starfish. One escape mechanism of these molluscs is the violent closing of their shells at the first scent of a starfish. By pushing water away, this snapping shut hurls the scallop backward in a form of jet propulsion, sometimes saving it from becoming starfish food.

even individuals may have a distinctive odor. Young fish use body patterns or scent for recognition when forming schools. For instance, silversides reared in isolation form schools within two hours after being placed in a tank with other fish of the same species. But, as with the other lower vertebrates (amphibians and reptiles) and invertebrates, the full battery of communicatory signals develops only in maturity.

Certain species of fishes secrete a chemical substance in their skin which is released when the fish is injured. The chemical spreads quickly in the water and acts as an alarm signal not only for the other fish in the school but for other species as well. Karl von Frisch, the noted German zoologist, isolated one of these chemicals and discovered that the barest trace amounts when placed in a laboratory aquarium will quickly frighten minnows and certain other species. Some odors produced by fishes attract others of their kind; other scents actually repel them. The attractants may bring opposite sexes together, and the repellents may drive rivals away.

In fishes, the sense of smell is extremely keen. It is their most important means of detecting things in their surroundings, and they can pick up an ordor even after it has been highly diluted by water. Olfactory sense organs are located in the nostrils. When the odor is detected, nerves transmit the stimulus from the nostrils to the brain for interpretation.

The sense of taste seems to be poorly developed in fishes; in fact, taste buds have been found in the mouths only of the lungfishes. However, some fishes—the catfish, for example— have a sensitive apparatus in their barbels, or chin whiskers, for detecting touch and scent. With this apparatus the catfish is able to locate chemical components representing food in the water. Researches conducted on the barbels of the bullhead, a small catfish, by biologists at the University of Michigan's Department of Wildlife and Fisheries revealed that fish kept in water saturated with detergents lost the ability to smell and, thus, the ability to find food.

Fishes and many other sea animals have earned an unfair reputation for being mute. A variety of reasons account for this situation. One reason is that most of the sounds these creatures make are beyond the range of human hearing. Another reason is that much of this underwater communication is in reaction to chemical and tactile stimuli—and the senses of scent and touch are less highly developed in man than in other animals. Continuing investigations into the secrets of how fishes and other aquatic animals survive in the "outer space" of the ocean are doing much to dispel our ignorance and are also providing us with answers to a number of questions that plague us here on terra firma.

3. Insects

Insects are believed to have lived on earth for about 300 million years before the first man made his appearance. During this time they evolved tremendous powers of adaptability that have enabled them to survive under a variety of hostile conditions. One way in which the nearly one million species of insects have adapted is through the development of their forms of communication.

The necessities of existence have formed the behavior patterns of insects. A wasp, for example, does not sting an enemy because it is "angry" but because it must defend itself; the honeybee does not forage for food because it is "industrious" but because it must provide for its hivemates; an ant does not develop a complex social organization because it is "wise" but because such organization is required for survival. And, like other aspects of their behavior, the forms of communication among insects result from internal and external influences as well as from the ability to imitate the actions of other insects. In the communicative process insects exploit the whole range of sensory signals, involving sight, sound, touch, taste, and scent; but they react with greatest sensitivity to sound and scent. Often insects employ compound signals to transmit specific information—as in the honeybees' "wagtail," or "waggle," dance, where both scent and touch are utilized to indicate the source of food.

How Insects Produce Sounds

Insects produce more percussive sounds, such as scraping and tapping, than sounds of any other kind. Many of these sounds appear to us to be nothing more than nonmusical noises; yet usually they are produced by structures that are highly specialized for the purpose and that serve the communicative functions of the insect very well.

One of the most common sound-producing mechanisms employed by insects is stridulation: the rubbing or scraping of one body part against another, often with great vigor and rapidity and in a distinctive pattern, frequency, and rhythm. This is the so-called "scraper-file" arrangement. About eighty or ninety toothlike projections, variously called spines, spurs, or pegs, range along one surface of the insect's leg or wing to form the file. Another part, often a wing, has a thickened, extratough vein, the scraper. The file is drawn back and forth across the scraper, much as a bow is drawn across the strings of a violin. Short-horned grasshoppers and locusts use this method almost exclusively. Two members of the long-horned grasshopper group—the tree crickets and the katydids—rub their forewings together.

The cicada is king when it comes to stridulatory mechanisms—and only the male can perform. "Happy the cicadas' lives," wrote Greek dramatist Xenarchus over two thousand years ago, "for they have voiceless wives." With two large vibrating membranes, or tymbal organs, in the thorax, the male produces a shrill, penetrating noise that varies in quality from a series of rapid clicks to almost a buzz. This sound travels over long distances. During the business of sound making, a large muscle attached to the center of the tymbal on its inner surface contracts and pulls the membrane inward with a loud click. When the muscle relaxes, the membrane snaps back and another sharp click is produced. The result is the same as that obtained by pushing the bottom of a tin can in and out with the fingers. The faster the contraction and relaxation of the tymbal muscle, the more the clicks seem to the human ear to blend into an almost continuous sound. Cicadas can contract their tymbal muscles at the rate of 100 to 500 times per second. Large air sacs on either side of the tymbals resonate freely when these organs are in use, thereby adding to the intensity of the sound.

One hot summer day the noted nineteenth-century French entomologist Jean Henri Fabre determined to discover whether the singing of a persistent group of cicadas could be disrupted by other noises. He went so far as to borrow the municipal artillery—two huge cannon—and persuaded the village gunner to come and fire them off.

The windows of Fabre's house were opened wide to prevent

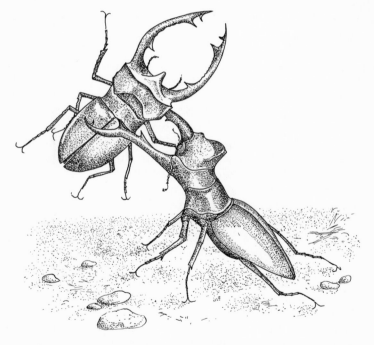

Conflict between males, with the victor mating a nearby female, is common among many types of animals. Such battles between male stag beetles often end when one lifts the other entirely off the ground and then throws him down again.

breakage, and the two "thundering engines" were placed in the yard near his front door. First one was touched off, then the other. The resulting blasts shook the countryside. The effect of this experiment on the neighboring populace is not recorded; but the cicadas, undaunted, sang on.

Since sound is transmitted better through solids than through air, beetles stridulate by stamping or bumping their heads or other parts of the body against the ground or on rotting wood, leaves, and such. Some drum their abdomens against the surface of the ground; others tap it with their forelegs. Stone flies have tiny malletlike structures on the tip of the abdomen which they use for this purpose.

Perhaps the most interesting of all the sound-producing mechanisms used by insects is the one depending upon the movement of air—the same principle on which the human voice relies. Air moves through the voice box, causing vocal membranes, or "cords," to vibrate and thus produce sound. Both sexes of the death's-head moth utilize direct air movement through the pharynx and the epipharynx to produce sound. When the muscles of the pharynx contract, air is alternately sucked in and blown out through the long, curved proboscis, or nose. Passage of the air between pharynx and epipharynx causes the air to pulse or throb. This pulsing, together with the subsequent resonating of the pharyngeal cavity, creates the noise. If the pharynx contains food, sound cannot occur. A moth having this highly specialized type of sound production apparatus can emit loud squeaking noises. Actually this is a most efficient type of stridulatory mechanism, since sound production requires relatively low energy output.

Although the orthopterans (which include the grasshoppers, crickets, katydids, cicadas, and others) make more noise than all the other insects combined, a few lepidopterans—butterflies and the moths mentioned above—produce sounds. The method by which they do so depends upon the species: some have frictional mechanisms, some use tymbal organs, and a few depend upon their ability to disturb the air in a series of pulses or throbs. Lepidopterans make up the only known insect group in which sound is produced in all stages of development—by egg, larva, pupa, and adult. In some cocoons, noises made by the scraping of the pupae against the interior surfaces can be heard by the human ear for a distance of several feet.

Insects are capable of a wide variety of flight sounds, some of which serve as signals in communication. Wing vibrations produce much of the noise made by flies, mosquitoes, and bees in flight. The range of frequency of beating insect wings is about four to a thousand beats per second. As the frequency of the wing beat rises, the sound becomes audible. The faster the vibration, the higher the pitch of the sound. Often, higher harmonics are produced by vibration and resonance in the thorax and in the wings themselves.

Experimental evidence suggests that honeybee sounds re-

Stephen Dalton
When the hive becomes too crowded, the reigning queen will leave in a swarm with half the workers. The remaining workers then set free one of the immature queens to replace her.

sult from wing vibrations. James Simpson, at Rothamsted Experimental Station, England, showed that when the bee's air holes are plugged, there is no change in sound quality. Adrian M. Wenner's investigations at the University of California at Santa Barbara revealed that clipping the wings causes alteration of the sound in direct proportion to the amount of wing removed. The more wing material removed, the higher the pitch and the lower the intensity of sound.

Wind affects the bee's distance judgment to some extent. Sound trains and pulses given by a bee that has flown against the wind to a food source will exaggerate somewhat the actual distance of that source from the hive. The reason for this is that the bee tends to fly at the same ground speed regardless of wind velocity. It attempts to overcome the wind effect by flying close to the ground; when the wind velocity approaches fifteen miles per hour, the bee gives up flying and voluntarily grounds itself in the hive.

How Insects Hear

The types of communicatory signals that insects can send and receive most effectively often depend upon the animal's sense organs and relative thresholds of sensitivity. If an insect has an acute sense of hearing, for example, it can usually make noises, and sound signals are used during communication. The exception to this is the moth. Most moths make no noises, yet their hearing is excellent—otherwise they could not detect the ultrasonic echo-locating sounds produced by the bats that prey upon them.

The world is a silent one for some insects, but many can detect vibrations transmitted through the substrate, that is, the water, soil, wood, or whatever that the insect happens to be sitting on. Many insects, too, can perceive sounds transmitted through air.

The most advanced type of vibration-detection device to be found among the insects is the tympanal organ. This tiny, drumlike structure is usually found in close association with large tracheae, or air ducts, and with bundles of sound-sensitive tissues known as chorodontal sensillae. The tympanal organs always occur in pairs, and each is capable of receiving and locating sounds from any direction. Thus if one of a pair is

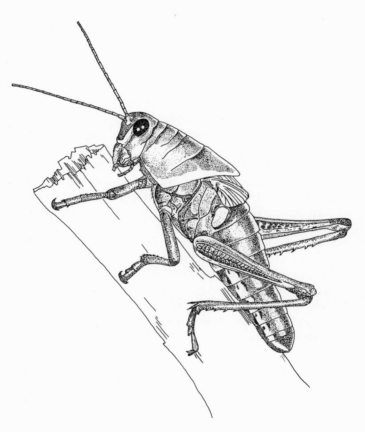

The light-colored oval area on the first abdominal segment of this immature grasshopper is its tympanic membrane, or hearing organ. There is another such membrane on the other side of the animal at the same point on the body.

destroyed, the other will still enable the insect to react appropriately to whatever call is being given.

Tympanal organs are found in the grasshoppers, cicadas, and locusts and in most moths. They are located on the abdomen or legs and not on the head, as one might expect. Although this hearing apparatus is far simpler in structure than man's, its range and discriminatory qualities are quite remarkable. For instance, even if the noise of a scraped file exactly matches the pitch of a cricket's chirp, a second cricket can readily discriminate between the two. Some insects are able to detect ultrasonic vibrations a good two octaves above those discernible to the human ear.

The vast majority of insects, however, do not possess such an elaborate and sophisticated hearing apparatus. They must rely on the antennae, or "feelers," to pick up sound vibrations. This is accomplished by means of specialized cells, known as Johnston's organs, which are grouped together at the base of the antennae. These organs are found among many different types of insects but are most highly developed in the mosquitoes and midges. Even when a man-made background noise is 100 times louder than the noise made by the insect, the flight sound of a female yellow-fever mosquito can attract a male of the same species. The male somehow is able to screen out and ignore the jamming effect.

Insects also hear by means of three other types of organs: (1) Hair sensillae, which exhibit vibration-detecting hairs on various parts of the body, are concerned mainly with touch sensations, although they probably receive airborne vibrations as well. (2) Chorodontal sensillae are scattered throughout the body, with many near the surface layer of cuticle, or body covering; these respond to airborne stimuli. (3) Subgenual organs, located on the legs of certain butterflies, grasshoppers, crickets, stone flies, antwasps, ants, and bees, are concerned primarily with low-frequency vibrations carried through the ground, nest floor, or other substrate. The ability to hear, however, is not inevitably linked with the ability to understand. For example, because the bee does not respond to sounds that are unrelated to visual and other stimiuli, investigators question its ability to interpret sound.

Auditory Signals

It is possible that insects were the first creatures upon earth to make sounds. Various kinds of stimuli cause an insect to "sound off." Sometimes it is the temperature: Because insects do not have a constant body temperature, their muscles work faster at higher temperatures than at lower ones. The frequency of the tree crickets' singing, for example, increases as the temperature rises. Count the number of chirps during 15 seconds, add 39, and you have the current temperature. To predict the number of chirps per minute, multiply the temperature by 4 and subtract 160.

The intensity of the light, the presence or absence of other insects, and even the sensation of being lightly touched constitute other stimuli. Many insects emit a raucous cry when captured by a predator, which may even startle the assailant into releasing its prey. Some bees, locusts, and gnats use sounds to help keep the swarm together. Other sounds are produced that can be interpreted as warning or danger signals, distress calls, and even the mimicking of other insects. Much of this sound production is associated with reproductive activity in one way or another. Usually the noises are made by males and directed toward females, although occasionally the female assumes the role of the singer. The mosquito attracts a mate by means of flight sounds; the stridulatory courtship call of the short-horned grasshopper indicates the territory the male will defend.

If a courting male grasshopper is interrupted by a second male, the first insect immediately changes from a calling song to an aggressive display known as the rival's song (or duet). The newly arrived male proceeds to sing a similar song, and the two stand "toe to toe" in a singing battle royal. Finally, either one of the males departs in defeat or the female grows weary of this dual rendition and seeks a mate elsewhere.

Grasshoppers rarely attack each other physically during a rival's song.

A sample of grasshopper talk—based on the values applied to the six chirps of the male grasshopper by Dr. Abraham Moles, a researcher into the language of animals—appeared in the British journal *Science* and was reprinted in an experimental British publication, *Tlaloc*, as found verse (defined as "unintentional verses from any prose"):

> it is fine—life is good
> i would like to make love
> you are trespassing on my territory
> she's mine!
> o how nice it would be to make love
> how nice to have made love.

Noise making is not confined to the larger insects. The tiny male fruit fly gives a mating call by vibrating an area of each wing across double rows of large bristles on the abdomen. If several males call simultaneously, the interested female approaches the one whose sound she detects first.

Even though the singing of individual members of an insect species is very much the same, subtle differences in songs exist even among closely related species. This helps to preserve the integrity of the species: because a female of one species will not answer the mating call of a male belonging to another species, hybridization does not normally take place—at least not in the wild. Hybrids have been propagated in the laboratory, however.

Most if not all species of ants give a warning or danger signal. The signal may involve stridulation, body position, scent, or a combination of these. Highly agitated, the ant giving the warning runs about the nest or trail, jaws open and abdomen elevated. Carpenter ants rattle their abdomens against the ground to warn of danger, and certain tree-dwelling ants tap their heads on the leaves when threatened. The resulting sound can be heard clearly from a few feet away.

Bees emit short, loud warning sounds when an ant or other

intruder enters the hive, and sharp buzzes when the hive is jostled. Guard bees produce the latter sound, and workers —sensing the alarm signals as vibrations in the hive—often follow with piping beeps spaced a half-second apart. The beeping may continue for several minutes, its function apparently being to soothe the excited colony.

Food-scouting bees use sound signals to tell other bees where to find food. In the honeybee, the wing vibrations that accompany strenuous wagging during the straight run of the wagtail dance transmit information about the distance of the food site from the hive. (Most of the credit for this discovery belongs to Adrian Wenner.) The stingless *Melipona* bees of tropical Brazil communicate food information primarily by means of sound, using a sort of Morse code to indicate distance from the food source. But the more primitive foragers of the genus *Trigona* leave only scent trails.

The sound spectrogram shows that honeybee stridulation occurs in surges, or trains, with about thirty-two pulses per train. Each pulse is made up of low-frequency vibrations of 250 cycles per second; about two and a half pulses occur during one waggle of the bee's posterior. In the darkness of the hive, other bees follow the dancer closely, touching their antennae to the latter's thorax.

Wenner found that the average number of pulses in a sound train and the average time length of sound trains during dancing are directly proportional to the distance between the food source and the hive. The low-frequency pulsing sounds supplement the waggles in conveying distance information. Sound, in fact, appears to be an integral part of the wagtail dance. In cases where a returning dancer performed silently, Wenner observed that the other bees followed the dance but that none flew off to the food source described.

Queen bees make piping noises that naturalists call "tooting" or "quacking." Only one mature queen is allowed in a beehive, and she does the tooting; the quacking is done by maturing queens trying to escape from their cells. As fast as one queen opens the cell, a worker closes it and seals it tight.

Now and then, a single maturing queen is allowed to leave the cell, and she promptly engages the old queen in mortal combat.

The reigning queen of a beehive tries to sting all the maturing queens to death while they are still in their cells. Sometimes the attempt succeeds; but often the workers intervene to prevent mass regicide. The frustrated queen toots her protests around the clock, sometimes for as long as a week. This sound grows louder and louder; after several days one can hear it when standing ten or twelve feet from the hive.

A spectrogram shows that the toots of the queen consist chiefly of sound vibrations in the order of 500 cycles per

Stephen Dalton
Social insects, such as bees, have a complex society with a highly developed system of communication. Each member has its own special job to perform. Here a worker feeds a queen larva.

second, accompanied by various overtones. This means that the tooting sound is remarkably similar to the sounds of human speech. Observed spectrographically, the toot actually lasts one second and is followed immediately by several shorter toots. The quack, on the other hand, is quite different. It starts with short sounds and ends with longer ones, and its basic frequency is considerably lower than 500 cycles per second. Queens respond by quacking to artificially produced tooting, but they completely ignore electronically produced quacking.

The tooting of the reigning queen and the quacking of the immature queens in their cells keep the workers informed concerning the number of free and potentially free queens in the hive. A colony of bees cannot survive without its queen; if, as often happens, the reigning queen suddenly leaves the hive with a swarm, the workers allow one of the quackers to emerge as a replacement.

Visual Signals

Some insects supplement auditory signals with visual ones when they give a cry of alarm. The peacock butterfly, for example, gives a warning sound and flashes open its wings with a hissing noise to display its so-called eyespots. This combination of auditory and visual signaling temporarily frightens away rats and mice, both of which are extremely sensitive to high-frequency vibrations. Courtship also may involve visual display. The male in some species of flies brings the female a gift. This may be a prey he has caught, wound up in silky threads; or the bundle may contain not food but flower petals; or the bundle may be empty.

Although most insects possess two types of eyes, their vision, generally speaking, is poor. The two large compound eyes are each made up of a number of facets that serve as individual lenses for each eye unit, or ommatidium. In some insects each eye may have as many as 20,000 ommatidia. A compound eye resembles a fixed-focus camera in that it cannot be focused sharply on near or distant objects. The insects with the keenest vision are those possessing the greatest number of facets. The three simple eyes, or ocelli, are usually located on the upper part of the head between the compound eyes. Even though some insects—butterflies, moths, and bees, for instance—can distinguish colors, most insect eyes perceive only light and dark. Bees see farther up into the ultraviolet range than we do but are blind to most of the wavelengths that appear red to us, and their discrimination of color shades is less accurate.

The most advanced form of visual signal is bioluminescence —the ability of some plants and animals to produce light by chemical means. It is employed by the common firefly, or "lightning bug." The nonflying larva and wingless female of some species are called glowworms. On warm summer evenings, it is a common sight to see these insects winking and blinking their soft greenish-white lamps over the lowlands, along ponds and streams, and in our yards and playgrounds. There are about 2,000 known species of fireflies (actually not flies at all, but beetles)—each with its own characteristics and signal pattern.

The pale, cold light produced by the firefly is associated with survival in that it serves as a signal to bring male and female together for mating. Male fireflies do more flying and lamp flashing than do females. To make their flashes visible from the greatest possible distance, the males fly with their bodies tilted upward at an angle of about forty-five degrees. Warm, humid weather seems to be favored for flashing. Sometimes hundreds, even thousands of fireflies synchronize their rhythms, producing huge flashes of light.

A firefly species can be distinguished by the duration of the flash or by the time interval between flashes. The male *Photinus pyralis*, for example, flashes in a more or less rhythmic pattern; the female waits for two seconds after seeing this signal to flash, and thus identify herself as belonging to the right species.

The light-producing organs are located at the tip of the abdomen, where a network of tiny air tubes connects with breathing holes. Light is produced when a substance called luciferin is oxidized in the presence of an enzyme, luciferase, which acts as a catalyst for the reaction. This organic catalyst is present only in minute, or trace, amounts and is used over and over again in the light-producing process.

The colors produced during bioluminescence vary with the type of insect making the light. Yellow, white, greenish-blue, reddish, and orange, singly and in various combinations, are the hues that commonly occur. The large luminous railway beetle of Paraguay produces a bright red light at each end of its body, with tiny green beacons distributed on other parts of its anatomy. Two brilliant greenish lights up front proclaim the presence of the little click, or fire beetle, also known as the "automobile bug," which occurs widely in Florida, Texas, and the Caribbean region.

The intermittent character of the firefly's luminescence is caused by the inhibitory action on its nerve impulses of a biochemical (protein pyrophosphate) in the insect's tail. The sending out of a "flash" signal by the nerve impulse releases an inorganic pyrophosphate that restrains the inhibitors and allows the active ingredients—luciferin, luciferase, oxygen, and adenosine triphosphate (ATP)—to interact and produce light.

Tactile Signals

The survival of any ant colony as a social group demands an extensive cooperation among individuals, much of it accomplished through the sense of touch. In ant society certain members—individuals that appear for some reason to have greater learning ability than their nestmates—act as leaders. These ants also have greater powers of retention, apparently "recalling" the exact location of old foraging grounds and trails even after having hibernated throughout the winter. Internal changes trigger certain behavioral patterns: the nest must be repaired or perhaps enlarged, food must be procured, and both the queen and the young require constant attention.

In every ant colony there is constant licking, nuzzling and caressing, and exchanging of regurgitated food. This exchange of nutrients is known as trophallaxis; probably the members of an ant colony are held together entirely by trophallactic relationships. Constantly waving antennae provide the ant with well-developed taste, smell, and touch senses. When one ant encounters another, each taps the other's antennae gently. Before an ant eats, it thoroughly examines the food material by palpating it with the antennae. The ant indicates to the aphid that serves as its "cow" exactly when to exude a drop of honeydew by poking the aphid's abdomen with its antennae. That these appendages are critically important to the ant is shown by the fact that the ant is forever cleaning them, using mouthparts and special comblike devices found on the legs.

Stephen Dalton
Ants in a colony are constantly touching one another—licking and nuzzling. Here two ants exchange food that has been eaten and regurgitated.

In the tropical rain forests of Africa, Asia, and Central America, army ants travel in colonies that may number over 100,000. Attempting to satiate their voracious appetites, they move over the ground as a unified mass. Each ant, with its antennae pointing forward and beating rhythmically, keeps its position in the formation. Certain light-colored members of the colony appear to serve as officers, keeping order and acting as advance scouts; darker-colored individuals perform as privates, following orders as though possessed of a remarkable sense of duty.

As anyone who has been on a picnic knows, food placed on a cloth spread on the ground is soon visited by a foraging ant;

Stephen Dalton
Ants leave scent trails by periodically touching their abdomens to the ground and depositing drops of liquid excreta. These harvester ants are following a scent trail back to their nest.

unless this scout is promptly disposed of, it will leave only to return with its relatives. The forager, obviously, has "told" the others of the food find and proves it by bringing them to the feast. Among the more primitive species, the scouting ant does not exchange tactile signals but carries the odor of the newly found larder to its nest mates, who in turn promptly follow this strong attraction to the food source.

The bees' senses of smell and touch are in their antennae, which perform an important function in their food dances. That the language of the honeybee is among the most elaborate and advanced in the animal kingdom—particularly with respect to food seeking and housing—is revealed by the work of Professor Karl von Frisch at the University of Munich, of Adrian M. Wenner at the University of California at Santa Barbara, and of many other diligent investigators.

Von Frisch wished to observe for himself the method a honeybee uses to pass along information to its hivemates about the direction in which they must travel to locate food and the distance from the hive that they will have to fly. He constructed a beehive with glass sides so that he could observe the bees inside as well as outside the hive. Knowing that from time to time bees leave the hive in search of food, Von Frisch provided them with a particularly attractive food source —a bowl of sugar-in-water solution near the hive. Then he began to watch.

Some time later, a foraging bee discovered the syrup and immediately proceeded to suck up a generous supply of its sticky goodness. Returning to the hive, the forager performed a "round dance" on the surface of one the honeycombs, describing circles first to the left and then to the right. After vigorously repeating these movements for thirty seconds or more, the bee moved to a new place on the comb and began to dance again.

The other workers became highly excited and followed the dance pattern, touching the dancer with their antennae to identify the scent of the food source. Soon one bee flew away from the hive, followed later by another and then another, until several had located the syrup. Eventually each returned to the hive, delivered food to his hivemates, and began a dance of his own. A sort of chain reaction had begun, and within a short time most of the bees in the hive were involved.

Von Frisch discovered that if he substituted for his rich sugar-water mixture a piece of filter paper or blotter merely moistened with the syrup, dancing did not occur. He also found that the sweeter he made the solution, the more vigorous the dance. When Von Frisch moved the food dish as far from the hive as 6,000 yards (3½ miles), the dance became more complex. Up to a distance of 100 yards, the simple round dance was performed; it told that food had been found but gave no information about direction or distance. For food sites beyond this distance, the dance took the form of a figure eight, with the dancer energetically wagging its tail when making the straight run between the two loops of the "eight."

The direction of this run indicates the direction to the food, Von Frisch discovered. The rhythm of the dance—the number of tail-wagging runs per unit of time—communicates the distance. A dance repeated ten times in fifteen seconds, for example, indicates that food is 100 to 200 yards away; when the dance slows down to four or five runs in fifteen seconds, food is 1,000 yards away. If the feeding area is in line with the position of the sun, the straight run is always performed straight up the surface of the honey comb; if the feeding area is located opposite to the direction of the sun, the run is aimed downward on the comb. For a feeding area of, say, forty-five degrees to the right of the sun, the dancer moves across the surface of the honeycomb at an angle of forty-five degrees with respect to the vertical axis.

Honeybees do not actually need to see the sun to carry out their dance. All they need is a small patch of blue sky. On cloudy days, so long as there is a break in the overcast, the dances go on uninterruptedly. But if there is no clear area above, the dances cease. The explanation for this phenomenon is that the eye of the bee can polarize sunlight: since the sunlight is perceived as directional rays, the insect easily orients itself to the position of the sun—even though it often cannot see the sun itself.

If the beehive is opened and the honeycomb is held in the hands during the so-called wagtail dance, the bee is not thwarted. If the comb is oriented in a horizontal instead of a vertical position, the bee performs the straight part of the dance, or the run, in a direct line with the food source; if the comb is then slowly rotated, the bee continues to indicate the direction of the food as efficiently as before.

Bees sometimes travel a mile or more from the hive to to collect nectar. Often hills, buildings, and other large obstacles obstruct the flight path. Undeterred, the scouting bee flies over the obstacle, and upon returning to the hive, dances out for the information of its mates the distance to the food, including the amount added by having to fly over the obstacle.

Misunderstandings because of "dialect" or geographical differences occur when bees of different races are placed in the same colony. For example, not only does the Italian bee dance more slowly than the Austrian bee, but it also performs a dance form—the sickle dance—that is unknown to its Austrian relative. Furthermore an Austrian bee flies too far for the food described by an Italian bee; when the dancer is Austrian, the Italian hivemate does not fly far enough.

The brooding behavior of honeybees is also dependent upon the use of tactile signals. After the queen has deposited her eggs in a wax comb, the larval bees must be fed by the workers. Through an intricate communication system of body movements and antennal contacts, the workers learn to recognize the solicitation signals of the larval bees as the latter solicit food from them.

When a bee population moves from the mother hive, former food scouts often become house hunters. Dr. Martin Lindauer, author of *Communication Among Social Bees*, describes how a swarm of bees assembles in a cluster near the hive it has left while scouts go forth to find possible nesting places. On their return to the cluster the scouts report their finds by means of a wagtail dance in which direction and distance are indicated. An especially desirable dwelling is announced by a dance of noticeable liveliness and length. Many of the bees, excited by the dance, fly off to inspect the various properties under consideration. One or two weeks may pass before the swarming cluster reaches agreement as to the best nesting place. To advertise this successful conclusion of their efforts, the scouting bees dance in unison. The swarming ends and the bees fly to their new home.

Chemical Signals

Certain species of bees, ants, cockroaches, moths, butterflies, and silkworms produce strong-smelling gases or fluids, either by means of special scent glands in the mouthparts or abdomen or as metabolic by-products. These chemical substances play a crucial role in the biology of social insects; used as signals between individuals, they are called pheromones.

Some of these substances are releaser pheromones, which produce a more or less immediate, though temporary, change in behavior and are believed to act via the signal recipient's receptors and central nervous system. These relatively simple volatile substances transmit their messages via the olfactory system; they form the basis of most short-term chemical signals in both social and nonsocial insects. Pheromones of this type include sex attractants and activants, alarm substances, and trail-laying scents.

Primer pheromones are transmitted by mouth and produce little or no obvious behavioral response. It has not been established whether they act directly on endocrine systems, in the manner of hormones, or are mediated by the taste receptors and central nervous system. These pheromones occur only in social insects, where they regulate the production of castes. To date, only one primer pheromone—the so-called queen substance, or royal jelly—has been identified.

The importance of pheromones in communal life among social insects has been emphasized by Dr. C. D. Michener, of the University of Kansas; Dr. Barry Philip Moore, of Australia's Commonwealth Scientific and Industrial Research Organization; and other investigators. Ants, bees, wasps, termites, and certain other insects live together as highly organized groups, or societies. Unlike a human society, which is made up of many families, an insect society is one huge family. All ants in an anthill or bees in a beehive, for example, are related. The social insects perform their tasks with what has been described as machinelike efficiency, and have developed complex systems and techniques of construction, agriculture, food storage, warfare, and slavery. Obviously these would not be possible without some form of equally highly organized communication. Within the insect society, pheromones regulate the development and behavior of each indi-

Female silkworm moths "call" their males by emitting a special scent. Here a male has responded to such a call by landing on a tree near a female of his species. The prominent eyespots visible on his wings serve to confuse would-be predators.

vidual much as hormones govern the cells of the human body. Among ants, wasps, and termites, association by trophallaxis is much more important than it is among bees.

Alarm scents are characteristically volatile and highly concentrated, for they need last only a short time. Several of these pheromones have been chemically identified: One of the excitant components of the honeybee's sting is iso-amyl-acetate; limonene is the alarm substance of the Australian harvester termite (*Drepanotermes rubriceps*); different species of ants are alerted by 2-heptanone, methyl heptanone, citral, and citronellal.

From the jaws of harvester ants, Oklahoma State University scientists extracted a chemical (4-methyl-3-heptanone) of a type known as ketones. This chemical is employed by the ants as a means of communication and alarm. When a small drop of the chemical was placed on an ant, the scientists reported that other ants passing within three or four centimeters of the treated individual immediately chased and attacked it.

A single agitated member of an ant colony can easily stir the whole colony into feverish excitement. The danger signal, whether it be a scent, stridulation, body position, or any combination of these, usually is unspecific as to implication. When it is given, some individuals in a nest rush about in all directions looking for food; others begin tending the queen or brood; and still others start to make repairs on the nest.

Releaser pheromones play an important part in direction finding and attraction to food sites among the social insects, especially those that forage for food. The scouts of a few of the more advanced species leave a scent trail from the food source to the nest as a guide to the other ants. Touching their abdomens to the ground at intervals, they deposit droplets of liquid excreta; ants following this trail reinforce the scent by pressing their own abdomens to the ground. When chemicals are removed from an ant trail, the column ceases to move in the right direction. Other pheromones mediate such responses in ants as colony recognition, trophallaxis, and disposal of the dead.

Although only the higher termites forage for food, Dr. Moore discovered scent glands, for laying scent trails, in all the termite species he examined. A long-lasting scent-trail pheromone common to several Australian species of *Nasutitermes* has the constitution of a diterpenoid (C_{20}) hydrocarbon; it is present in the termites at a level of approximately one part in 4 million, and is effective in concentrations of from 10^{-5} to 10^{-8} gram per milliliter of inert solvent.

Perception of the plane of polarized sunlight is the basis for direction finding in honeybees, which transmit information about food source locations by means of the wagtail dance. To attract others to newly discovered food sites, however, worker bees use a pheromone from their Nassanoff gland, located on the upper side of the abdomen. Geraniol, citral, and nerolic acid are the principal chemicals involved.

Two Cornell University professors, Drs. Thomas Gisner and Jerrold Meinwald, have found that chemical defenses comparable to those of the skunk are widespread among arthropods (insects, spiders, and the like). Gisner and Meinwald claim that "the vocabulary of protective chemical signals possessed by these animals may be one of the richest in the entire world of life." Insects deliver their "stand clear" message to enemies in a variety of ways. The darkling beetle, with spraying glands on the underside of its rear end, must stand on its head to aim at an adversary. Even nonspraying beetles mimic this headstand as a warning to predators. The defensive spray directed by termite "soldiers" against invaders of their nest or territory not only incapacitates the enemy but also alerts the other soldiers to form a supplementary spraying force.

Most present-day nonsocial insects lead independent lives except for mating and gathering together for such purposes as hibernation. Aggregations of breeding populations are caused to collect through the release of pheromones. After feeding on a suitable host tree, for example, the male pine bark beetle produces a chemical substance that attracts both sexes to the tree. Apparently this pheromone is a blend of several related monoterpenoid (C_{10}) alcohols resulting either from the insect's metabolism or from constituents in the host tree.

Scientists have long been amazed by the male moth's ability to locate a mate over considerable distances. During the mating season, most female insects use odors to attract the male. In the nectar-feeding butterflies that are active during the daytime and in which visual perception of flower varieties and potential mates is important, the development of sex activants is limited. These chemicals become increasingly important in nocturnal, nectar-feeding moths, and reach their highest stage of development in species that do not feed at all during the adult stage. The female Austral vaporer moth (*Orgyia anartoides*), for example, lost her wings in the course of evolution and is entirely dependent on her sex-attractant pheromone for finding a mate. The male detects the minute amount released by means of sensitive olfactory receptors in his feathery antennae, and flies toward the source.

Some of the scents produced by insects are incredibly potent. Hubert and Mable Frings have reported that the female of certain silkworm moths gives off a scent that is effective as a lure in concentrations of as little as 10^{-10} microgram per milliliter. This is equivalent to only $\frac{1}{80,000,000,000,000}$ ounce per gallon. In the case of the gypsy moth, a few hundred molecules of gyptol, the female sex attractant, per cubic centimeter of air (about one part in 10^{17}) is sufficient to elicit a response from the male. Only males of closely related species are attracted by a given lure, and these species are kept apart in nature by seasonal and ecological differences.

The center of the complex organization common to the social insects is the queen (or, in the case of termites, the royal pair). The honeybee queen produces many pheromones, most of them with her mandibular glands; of these the queen substance has been identified as 9-keto-2-trans-decanoic acid. As a primer substance, its presence acts somewhat as a territory enforcer and chemosterilant in that it inhibits the ovarian development of the worker bees and the rearing of new queens by workers. When the concentration of the queen substance falls below the threshold level—for example, as part of the swarming cycle or as a result of the aging of the reigning queen—new queens are quickly produced. Worker bees eagerly seek the queen substance from the queen and from each other, thus assuring that it will be distributed uniformly about the hive. This pheromone also serves in a releaser role when used as a sex lure for drones on the mating flight.

Considering their often infinitesimal size, the great number of species and individuals, and the social organization achieved by many of the higher forms, insects have adapted with great success to the world about them. In some respects the communal organization of social insects is more truly a society than is that of humans. An insect society could not be formed and could not survive, any more than could human society, without communication between its members—the response of each individual to the others' presence. Continuing investigations into their communication patterns dramatizes clearly the efficient way in which the social insects face and master their environment.

4. Reptiles and Amphibians

Although Eve and the serpent carried on a memorable conversation in the Garden of Eden, and Mr. Toad chats his way through Kenneth Grahame's *The Wind in the Willows*, in reality reptiles and amphibians communicate on a relatively low level. Because they demonstrate little or no parental care, at least one category of signals—those between parents and young—is virtually eliminated. The undersized brains of reptiles and amphibians also undoubtedly contribute to the lack of complex patterns in their communication.

Reptiles

Comparatively few species of reptiles possess sound-producing mechanisms of any type. Those that do (for example, the lizardlike tuatara of New Zealand, which grunts and croaks) apparently evolved these mechanisms independently of one another. Because the hearing of most reptiles—especially that of snakes—is poor, it is no surprise that they rely more upon chemical and visual signals in communication than upon auditory ones.

Auditory Signals

Although they are not noted for their vocalization, snakes produce a variety of noises. Hissing is associated with snakes as a warning signal. The usual warning hiss is produced by the snake's forcibly expelling air from its lungs; but some snakes, however, have progressed further along the evolutionary path and have developed a membrane near the opening to the glottis. By expelling air across this membrane and thus causing it to vibrate, a long string of short hisses is produced in machine-gun fashion. So far as is known, this is the snake's closest approach to vocal sound.

Certain snakes—the African puff adder is one—have developed air-expulsion sounds to a high degree: this reptile makes a noise that is reported to sound like the snorting of a horse. The hog-nosed snake combines hissing and striking in a mock attack. If this bluff fails to produce the desired effect, the snake "plays dead"; opening its mouth wide, it goes into convulsive contortions, flips over on its back, and goes limp. Once the danger is past, the snake turns over on its belly again and glides away.

African egg-eating snakes, as well as certain Asian and African vipers, produce a rasping stridulation by grating together their scales, which are equipped with saw-toothed spines. To accomplish this feat, the reptile inflates its lungs so that the serrated spines press against one another as the snake characteristically writhes and wriggles.

Some snakes threaten their enemies by the simple expedient of rapidly vibrating their tails. The North American rattlesnake adds sound to its performance—an unsettling whirr, produced by the horny rattles at the tip of its tail. This warning mechanism is found in only two genera of snakes indigenous to the United States: *Crotalus* and *Sistrurus*. *Crotalus*, the more widely distributed of the two, includes the timber rattler, Western and Eastern diamondbacks, sidewinder, and prairie rattlesnake, and about fifteen others in the United States alone. Almost certainly the rattlesnake does not hear

New York Zoological Society
This western diamondback rattlesnake wards off his enemies
by rapidly vibrating his tail. The characteristic whirring noise
is produced by the horny rattles.

its own rattle. Because reptiles possess no external ear openings, they can respond only to vibrations passing through the
ground and, subsequently, through the bones of their heads.

Unlike snakes, lizards have ear openings on the sides of the
head. Geckos, a large family of tropical lizards, are the only
truly vociferous reptiles. A clicking sound, described as almost deafening, is ascribed to a gecko found in Africa. Most of
the sounds geckos make are related to territorial defense or
mating. With wide-open mouths and staring eyes, they squawk
loudly while making aggressive lunges toward an enemy. Although these reptiles are small—six inches or less in length—
this combination of sound and visual display usually proves
effective in discouraging an intruder. At least one species of
gecko produces a cricketlike stridulation by rubbing together
plates evolved for this purpose.

In the spring the loud bellowing of the bull alligator or
crocodile fills the air. Vibrating its body as it bellows, the bull
rises on its hind legs, then slowly sinks back. These hair-

raising bellows serve as mating calls and also keep other males aware of territorial boundaries. Crocodilians also hiss loudly when threatening another of their own species or intruders of a different species. Alligators have a short, loud alarm call that they give when frightened. When this cry is emitted by one member of a group, all members make a dash for the water.

American Museum of Natural History
The cobra, by flattening and expanding the skin on its neck, forms this menacing hood. In this manner the snake manages to appear larger than it really is.

Many turtles and tortoises manage a hiss of warning or threat, but few go beyond this. The mating call of the giant Galápagos turtle is a distinctive deep, hoarse roar; that of certain land tortoises consists of loud, repetitious rasping noises.

Young alligators begin communicating with their mother immediately upon hatching. For nine to ten weeks the eggs are incubated in a mound of mud and rotting swamp vegetation; then as the lengthy process of hatching gets under way, soft, squeaking cries for help can be heard. The mother responds by digging the mound open with her snout. Young alligators and crocodiles have been known to remain near their nesting site for as long as two months after hatching, still demanding their mother's attention in unsynchronized chorus, with raucous croaks and high-pitched grunts replacing the infantile squeaks. This is a risky business on the part of the young alligators; for the longer they remain near their mother, the greater the likelihood that one day she will walk up to them and eat them.

Visual Signals

As a rule, snakes do not see things in terms of form and color but in terms of movement. The lenses of their eyes are tinged with yellow, rendering their vision more acute. Not all have the same degree of acuteness; for example, the species that hunt their elusive prey in the open require keener sight than do the burrowing species.

Snakes use visual and auditory signals as warning devices. For example, when giving a threat or warning, the cobra of India flattens and expands the skin on its neck to form its familiar "hood." This gives the cobra the appearance of being larger than it really is; in addition the design on the back of the hood, which vaguely resembles an animal's face, helps to prevent attack from the rear.

Certain snakes perform a stereotyped dance that noted herpetologist Archie Carr, of the University of Florida, calls the "combat dance." The rattlesnake, a terrestrial reptile, per-

This is the "sparring" stage of a combat "dance" between two male western diamond rattlesnakes. These battles are like wrestling matches rather than striking or biting contests. They end when one snake becomes exhausted and crawls away.

forms the dance on land; the water moccasin (often referred to as the cottonmouth because of the whitish appearance of the inside of its mouth) does a modified, and more interesting, version in the water. The significance of the display is not known, but it may be a contest to determine territorial rights, mating rights, or social dominance relationships.

Animals generally bolt when startled or approached too closely. If man or animal approaches a group of sunning pond or river turtles, only one turtle need become frightened and dive into the water for the others quickly to follow suit.

To achieve the actual copulation shown here, the male banded gecko usually performs a display dance whenever he encounters another gecko during the mating season. If the other animal is also a male, it responds with a similar display and no copulation takes place. If it is a female, it reacts passively and mating occurs.

The dive itself serves as a danger signal. Undoubtedly the same form of subtle communication exists between turtles in nesting aggregations, which—as in the case of a sea turtle known as the Atlantic ridley—sometimes reach an estimated population of 40,000.

When frightened, the horned lizard (popularly but erroneously called the horned toad) may squirt a thin stream of blood from the corners of its eyes. It tends to go to extremes when angered, either puffing itself up or flattening itself out.

True chameleons, which change color seemingly to reflect their mood, often change their pattern as well. When one male meets another, each turns broadside, displays his colors, inflates his throat, and opens his mouth slightly. But actual physical conflict is rare.

Visual communication plays an important part in the male

Hissing loudly, the Australian frilled lizard spreads his great tooth-edged membrane to scare off an attacker. The yellow, scarlet, and steel-blue frill, sometimes almost as wide as the lizard is long—together with his wide-open, hissing red mouth —make up this harmless creature's sole defense against hungry enemies.

lizard's courtship display. As a major part of this display, some lizards adopt a peculiar way of walking or bow their necks upward in an exaggerated manner. Others have special fins or membranes on their backs, which they raise as part of their nuptial finery. Still others take on vivid colors during the mating season or display their normal coloration in a unique manner to attract a mate.

Chemical and Tactile Signals

Snakes and lizards have delicate senses of smell and taste, which are much more highly developed than in the crocodilians. Contrary to popular belief, the snake's tongue is not used to sting but to supplement the regular sense of smell

In many animals certain parts of the body have developed into lures to attract prey. Only the alligator snapping turtle, however, has a lure inside its mouth. This wormlike growth on the middle of the tongue moves slowly back and forth while the animal, mouth agape, lies motionless on the muddy bottom of some river or lagoon. The approaching fish sees only a worm in a rocky crevice and swims down to eat it, to be caught himself as the powerful beak snaps shut.

through the nostrils. The flicking tongue picks up odor particles from the air and carries them to two cavities in the mouth, called Jacobson's organs, that are lined with sensory cells.

When alarmed, the garter snake secretes a musky fluid from glands near the base of its tail. Musk and mud turtles emit an unpleasant musky odor as a warning signal. Other reptiles use scent to attract a mate. The bull alligator, for example, accompanies his bellows and rearings with a powerful scent released from glands under the lower jaw. This putrid odor hangs over the swamp like a fog. A similar scent is emitted by some female turtles to inform males of their presence, as well as by courting males to warn off rivals. Much of the reptiles' courting behavior, in fact, seems to be concerned primarily with aggressive display—threatening and driving away rival suitors—rather than with wooing and winning a mate.

Amphibians

About 335 million years ago, the amphibians were the first animals with backbones to leave their watery homes for life on land. This attempt was only partially successful, for these animals have never become entirely independent of water.

Only three groups of amphibians exist today: the frogs and toads, the salamanders, and the blind, wormlike caecilians of the tropics. Most amphibians spend part of their lives on land and part in fresh water. Structurally and functionally, they belong between the reptiles and the fishes. All have legs, lungs, and nostrils, and their sense organs can operate in both air and water.

Amphibians are the lowest order of vertebrates to have a larynx. During sound production, air expelled from the lungs passes over the vocal cords and enters the mouth region.

Resonance is added in some species (the tree frogs, for example) by vocal sacs placed variously under the throat or near the angles of the jaw. Many modifications of vocal sacs exist, including internal, external, and intermediate forms. This may be a result of natural selection, especially when differences are seen in closely related species. Amphibians with no vocal sacs are considered to be the most primitive; often they are totally aquatic.

Auditory Signals

The only sound makers among the amphibians are the frogs, toads, and tree frogs—the anurans, or "tailless," as the ancient Greeks described them. But the anurans include about 2,000 species, many of which are only seasonally vociferous, and others voiceless altogether. Among the latter (in common with certain other species) the tympanum, or middle ear, is lacking, thus drastically reducing hearing ability. Frogs that lack outer and middle ear parts can often emit feeble, squeaky calls. These primitive vocalizations are always given while the animal is submerged and depend upon the excellent transmitting qualities of water to carry them to their intended listeners.

Salamanders are notably silent; a few, however, produce very faint squeaking noises, and at least two can make sounds best described as soft whistles. Some of these sounds may be mating calls. One California species is reported to possess vocal cords and to be able to produce weak barks. These barks, which probably are part of a defense mechanism, last about 0.3 second each and are made up of about a dozen pulsations of approximately 3,100 cycles per second. One species of lungless salamander that lives in trees and is found chiefly in California produces a squeak that lasts less than 0.2 second. The animal apparently manages the pulseless sound by suddenly forcing air from its mouth.

The frog's tympanum, or eardrum, is a large, round disk visible on the sides of its head. In a very few species it is covered by nonadherent skin; but in most species the membrane is in direct contact with the environment. At least one species has an external ear canal, and the tympanum is located several millimeters deep in the head. Some species of frogs can detect sounds in the frequency range of 30 to 15,000 cycles per second.

For a long time salamanders were believed to be incapable of hearing airborne sounds; but training experiments have shown that some North American species can perceive differences in pitch on the order of a musical fifth. One variety shows response to frequencies up to 244 cycles per second. Salamanders probably receive vibrations by means of specialized cutaneous veins in the head region; the vibrations pass over these and other veins to either the oval window or the "ear" ossicles.

The role of vocalization in the life of amphibians is complex. Environmental factors, both internal and external, and the state of evolution of a species all affect the types of sounds produced. Internal environmental factors include mainly those associated with hormonal balance, especially during estrus, when the female is in heat. External factors include rain or the lack of it, temperature, relative humidity, and so on.

Frogs give calls for the effect of bringing a group together, distress calls, calls of warning, mating calls, release calls, and calls relating to territorial defense. Even so-called rain calls have been reported. Often frogs begin vocalizing in response to noises from a wide variety of non-anuran sources —such as airplanes, automobile engines, brush fires, and human imitations of their calls. Female frogs and toads may croak or scream; but only males call.

Young frogs are silent until they reach sexual maturity. Then, during the warm, wet spring and early summer, they come to the breeding site and begin calling to attract females and other males, or perhaps simply to defend their territories. Each species of frog or toad has a distinctive call.

Researches on that harbinger of spring, the spring peeper, first revealed the structure of the frog chorus. It was discovered that frogs sing in groups of three, and that a large chorus may be made up of many trios. In each trio a single frog sounds the note A a number of times; after a short pause, if there is no answer, he trills. Once a frog has trilled, a second frog commonly calls on the note G-sharp. Both frogs then alternately give their respective notes—A, G-sharp, A, G-sharp—for an indefinite length of time. If a third frog does not begin calling, the two discontinue their alternating calls, and after a pause the G-sharp caller emits a trill. At this sound a third individual starts giving a call on the note B. The three continue calling, each giving its respective note in the order A, G-sharp, B indefinitely. Duets are heard in the calls of some species.

German peasants are said to believe that each pond has a leader—the frog with the loudest croak—which acts as "choir director." Other than this bit of folklore, there appears to be no evidence of a social hierarchy among anurans such as exists in some other animals.

Frog mating calls are repeated over and over, often in chorus. Whether a frog is approaching a potential mate or a food supply, "first come, first served" is the order of the day. He simply reaches out and seizes the first passerby. Although in many cases mating calls of male frogs also perform the function of warning rivals to stay away, actual fighting over a mate is not known to occur. If a male frog is seized by mistake, he emits a loud squawk, known as the male release call, and begins to tremble violently. If the clasped female is not in a receptive state, she promptly utters a release cry and trembles or vibrates in a similar manner.

Mating calls of frogs and certain other anurans are of three types: a "trill," consisting of separate impulses; a "lone" call, emitted with more or less regularity; and a call consisting of a combination of these. To be effective a frog call must have a series of regular pulsations or interruptions. This feature is also common to the mating calls of many other animals, especially those of insects and birds.

Anuran mating calls range from the bass bellow of the bullfrog to the popping noises of the American spadefoot toad to the chirps of the tree frogs. The frog's mouth is closed when he gives the call, and vocalization is sometimes performed underwater. In some species the female also vocalizes during mating activities; but usually the arrangement parallels that found in so many other animals—the male calls, and the female comes to him. Upon approaching an aggregation of hundreds of chorusing males in a Florida pond, a female frog may be bombarded by the simultaneous mating calls of perhaps fourteen separate and distinct species. From this maze of discordant sounds she must, and does, select a mate of her own species. On rare occasions she does not, and hybridization occurs. The hybrid offspring, when matured, calls in a manner intermediate between the calls of the parents' species. In some species the female does not rely upon sound signals alone but utilizes the visual and chemical senses as well. There is evidence that the hearing range of some female frogs is so limited, they may not be able to hear the male's call at all.

By means of the spectrogram and sound tape recordings, amphibian calls have been found to vary among geographically separated members of the same species in such qualities as timbre (harmonic intensity variations), length of call, pitch, repetition rate, and pulse and trill rates.

In addition to serving as attractants, frog calls are also used to give warnings, to signalize distress, in defense of territory, and so on. I have often noticed in the field that when I startle a frog into hiding in the water, he usually gives a low croak or chirp as he leaps. This is a warning signal to neighboring frogs; and the splash made as the first frog enters the water serves to reinforce this signal.

I used to hear another type of frog call during boyhood fishing trips with an uncle. We would walk for miles to a remote creek to fish, looking forward to cooking our catch, if any, over a campfire. Particularly if the evening was warm and humid, we could hear a distinctive call, rather high pitched and given with apparent urgency. "Those frogs," my uncle would announce, "are calling for rain." I have since discovered that these calls are given at any and all times of the day or night, usually in warm, humid weather.

It is possible that these so-called rain calls are among the calls given by frogs to establish and defend territories. As part of its territorial defense (except during the breeding season), the pig frog emits intermittent grunts. The vocalization of the Texas cliff frog resembles that of certain birds or the stridulation of a cricket.

If the call is given with the frog's mouth open and is rather high in pitch, it is known as a "call of distress" or "scream of pain." A frog—female as well as male—utters this call when captured by a raccoon, turtle, snake, or other predator or when seized by the human hand.

Visual Signals

Some species of frogs seem to be gradually losing their voices, and may vocalize only in situations involving stress. Obviously they are using other types of signals, such as visual and olfactory, in order to communicate—else they could not survive. *Rana temporaria*, for instance, congregates at the breeding place without an audible sound. Only after amplexus has been accomplished do the males vocalize, and even then their call is of extremely low intensity.

Frogs that do not vocalize use odors for purposes of gathering together, then visual displays involving body movements and/or special coloration when male and female approach within visual range of each other. The frog's specialized optical system allows only the most selective information to register on the animal's consciousness, so that it sees only the configuration, movements, and distance of what it must see—whether it be food supply or mate.

During the breeding season the pigmentation of the anuran's throat often takes on bright coloration. Brilliant yellow and black predominate, the female throat being the more vividly pigmented and usually darker than that of the male. The female of a Venezuelan species makes a prominent display of her bright yellow throat when defending her home feeding grounds. At the approach of an intruder, she hops forward aggressively, displaying her rhythmically throbbing throat. If the outsider fails to heed this obvious warning and refuses to vacate the premises, the defending female leaps atop the challenger. At this the latter usually beats a hasty retreat. Occasionally, however, a fight ensues, ending only when one of the pair retires to a position outside the disputed territory. The purpose of such territorial defense is to regulate population densities and so insure that an area does not acquire more frogs than it can support.

There is even greater variation in site selection than in the types of calls produced by unrelated species. The place a frog chooses from which to vocalize is a part of its visual display. Some frogs and toads display themselves on rocks and ledges; others hide underground. Some prefer to call while beneath the surface of the water, others while only partly submerged. Some hide in tall grass or seek shelter under low-hanging limbs and brush. A position that dominates the surrounding area—such as the bluff bank of a river, or even trees—is the site selected by some anurans. Others sit in shallow water at the edge of a pond or stream. At least a few species do their vocalizing at a considerable distance from the water.

Chemical Signals

According to some biologists, the strong odors given off by ponds and sluggish streams serve as chemical signals attracting frogs to breeding grounds. The odors emanate from essential oils in algae, decaying matter, and so on. On several occasions frogs have been observed to travel relatively long distances over land to a breeding pond; others have been seen to float down creeks for several miles until in proximity to an unseen pond, emerge from the water, climb a steep bluff, and continue overland to the pond.

As a defense measure, or when in pain, the toad secretes an acid fluid from the parotoid glands (which constitute two large swellings, one behind each eye). The foot-long Colorado toad squirts its poison twelve feet. So effective is this defense that, it is claimed, dogs that have attacked a toad once never do so again. One species of salamander, on the other hand, uses scent secreted from special glands on the head in its aquatic mating activities. The male faces the female, flips his tail over his head, and thrashes it about vigorously; this creates a water current around his head to carry his scent to the female.

These relatively uncomplicated forms of communication in reptiles and amphibians have as their primary aim the preservation of the species. As is true among other higher animals, selection is the prerogative of the female, who must seek out a mate of her own species. In this, specific signals play a crucial role, helping to deter interbreeding and hybridization.

Stephen Dalton
The toad defends himself by secreting an acid fluid from the parotoid glands, located one behind each eye.

Signals that differentiate clearly among the species also give both young and adults a greater chance for survival by enabling them to take advantage of food supplies, warn off intruders, and avoid danger. Similar communicatory patterns exist on a much more elaborate and highly developed scale among birds.

5. Birds

Because they are the most visible of the animals, the communication patterns of birds have been the most readily observed and studied. Virtually all birds communicate: with other individuals of their own species, with birds of other species, with mammals, and with man. They do so by means of sounds —usually vocal but sometimes nonvocal, such as wing noises —and by means of visual signals, such as special coloration or elaborate movements known as displays. Though their hearing is good and their visual sense often extremely keen, little if any communication among birds is known to be mediated by the senses of smell and taste.

Birds living in large aggregations or flocks have a much wider repertory of auditory and visual signals than do those that spend most of their time alone. Solitary birds (some of the cuckoos, for instance) have only one call or song, and it is used only during one short period of the year—the mating season. Few sounds or visual signals are of great value for the survival of the signaler alone; but through the combined influence of mating calls, warning signals, courtship displays, and other communicatory actions, the species has a better chance of being perpetuated.

Most birds use warning signals to insure the survival of

the species. Before a flock of mallard ducks lands on a swamp lake, for example, a few individuals descend to survey the landing area. Then, by means of a specific call, they inform the remainder of the flock that it is safe to come in; otherwise, they give a warning signal and fly away. Hunters have long used the "all clear" call to their advantage by learning to imitate it, thereby enticing the fowl within range of their guns. Often the auditory signal of the hunter is reinforced by visual stimuli in the form of lifelike decoys. I can think of only a single instance in which the vocal signals of a bird do not constitute a survival mechanism: the cackle of a domestic hen when she lays her eggs. This action, which invariably calls attention to her nest, is completely contrary

American Museum of Natural History
Some shrikes mimic other birds; all have a loud, shrieking call. Perched on this log are four young loggerhead shrikes.

to the survival reaction of wild birds, which try to keep the nesting place secret.

Only man, certain birds, and cetaceans (such as dolphins and porpoises) can mimic sounds that are foreign to them. Each group has a distinctive sound-producing apparatus.

The human voice box is the larynx, situated at the upper end of the trachea, or windpipe. Instead of a larynx, birds have a sound box, called the syrinx, at the base of the windpipe. The beak and tongue have little to do with voice production. Birds without a syrinx—the stork and the American vulture, for example—are voiceless; in fact, except for the incidental noises produced by their flapping wings, they make almost no sounds at all.

As a general rule, the more complex the bird's vocal apparatus, the more elaborate the song. The usual syrinx is a more or less rigid structure of cartilage or bone containing membranes, which are caused to vibrate when air is passed over them. From one to several pairs of muscles are found in the syrinx and surrounding area. Contraction and expansion of these muscles enable the bird to increase and decrease tension in the membranes of the syrinx, and so vary the quality of the sound produced as air rushes over them. In certain birds—the trumpeter swan is one—the long, contorted windpipe gives added resonance.

A bird's ear, like that of a mammal, is made up of an external, a middle, and an inner ear. But instead of three tiny ossicles, or bones, the bird's middle ear contains only a single, rod-shaped bone, the columella. This ossicle transmits sound vibrations from the eardrum directly to the oval window of the inner ear.

Generally speaking, birds have a good sense of hearing. Their overall hearing range is thought to be between 40 and 29,000 cycles per second; however, these are extremes. The average lower limit of the range for the dozen species tested was about 400 cycles per second; the upper limit was approximately 12,700 cycles per second. The hearing of birds of prey often is quite acute—or at least is attuned to the

Many animals have special sensory capabilities to fit their particular mode of life. The night-hunting saw-whet owl can see and hear his prey in what for a man would be utter darkness and complete silence. His hearing is especially sensitive in the range of typical mouse squeaks. The saw-whet's predatory success is also aided by soft plumage, which allows virtually soundless flight.

sounds made by their potential victims. Owls, for example, have excellent hearing in the high-frequency range of mouse squeaks (about 18,000 cycles per second). Too, hearing may be highly specialized. Baby chicks can hear almost nothing except the 400-cycle clucks of the mother hen; they cannot even hear themselves cheep. The hen, on the other hand, is extremely sensitive to the sounds produced by her chicks, which are at a level of 3,000 cycles or higher.

Auditory Signals

Distinguishing between what a scientist terms true bird song and the other vocal sounds of birds is not always an easy task. According to the English ornithologist William H. Thorpe, of Cambridge University, song is defined as the note or notes of a bird vocalization aranged in a rather definite pattern. A call, on the other hand, is brief, and patterning is extremely simple or lacking altogether.

The male does most of the singing; if both sexes have voices, the male's song is the more outstanding in complexity and intensity. The female cardinal and rose-breasted grosbeak, for instance, sing well, but their song is not as elaborate or perfected as that of the male.

Birds do most of their singing in early morning and late afternoon, remaining relatively quiet during the middle of the day. Morning singing usually differs somewhat from that at midday or in the afternoon. Humidity, temperature, and length and relative brightness of the day seem to have their effect upon the production of testosterone, the male sex hormone—and subsequently upon the song. During any non-mating season of the year, injection of testosterone preparations cause birds to sing; but the induced song is never complete. Several phrases are always missing—those that would have been included in the typical spring song.

The song a bird sings during the mating season is the complete primary, or full, song. At other times of the year the song is much shorter, and the bird seems to be rehearsing or "keeping in voice"; this is his secondary song, or subsong. The subsong, like the full song, is probably influenced by hormone production and has little if any communicatory function.

Although songs of birds within a species are basically very similar, individual birds in a flock made up of members of the same species can often recognize one another by their songs, owing to variations in the overall pattern. Some species have many variations: for example, about 900 have been recorded for the song sparrow. A. A. Saunders, who did the recording, noted that individual birds gave up to twenty versions of the basic song. Birds of closely related species often have songs that sound very much alike to the human ear. Few naturalists can identify even a small number of bird species accurately merely by listening to their songs; for exact identification, visual examination of the bird or study of a sound spectrogram is required. The songs of birds of the same species are often found to differ between groups far removed from each other. The song of the chaffinch in South Africa, for instance, differs markedly from that of the New Zealand species.

Although considerable variation among individuals and groups of birds often exists, there seem always to be enough typical characteristics by which to identify the species. Often a bird veers from its specific song, seemingly trying out a new repertoire.

The primary (complete) song of a bird is thought to accomplish the following functions, all of which are related to reproduction: (1) announce the sex of the singer and show that he is aggressive and energetic; (2) cause the sex of nearby birds to be revealed; (3) attract a mate; (4) lay claim to a territory, and maintain this claim; (5) bring about one or more matings; (6) establish and maintain (for a varying length of time) a strong social bond between members of a mating party; (7) carry on "conversation" concerned with daily routine, such as nest building and care of the young; (8) provide the individual with a means of identification to others in the family after the young are hatched.

Considered from another aspect, bird vocalization can be categorized as follows: (1) songs involved in social activities; (2) songs concerned with the life and development of the individual. If all the songs and nonsong vocalizations are taken into consideration, these two categories would include such communications as cries of alarm or fear, cries of pleasure, cries of distress, feeding calls, flocking calls, cries of aggression, nesting calls, flight calls (which differ from flocking calls), and cries of hunger—or "begging" calls—made by the young.

Although the primary song of a bird lacks individuality in its overall pattern, being made up of a preset series of notes ranging from one to many, it must be long enough not only to contain the basic sounds but to allow for individual variations. Voice quality, rhythm, and frequency of performance are among the most important factors in bird song. The way in which the various parts of the song are arranged or grouped together is also important, as are the intensifying of certain parts of the song and the minimizing of other parts.

If there is one factor that prevents the interbreeding of closely related species of birds, it is the difference in the song (or nonsong) vocalizations from one species to another. During the time it has taken birds to evolve to their present state, songs necessarily have had to become increasingly elaborate in order to do their part in maintaining the biological integrity of the species.

Each component or series of components in a song has its own specific function. For instance, the components that give directional information are produced in notes of low frequency. Since a bird's hearing, like ours, is stereophonic, direction is determined chiefly by relative differences in amplitude as the sound reaches the ears.

Even though it is usually the male bird that does the

vocalizing, the females of a few species—particularly those in which the courtship procedure is begun by the female instead of the male—have songs and calls. Certain quails, coucals, and snipes belong in this category. Female wrens and robins also sing at certain times of year, although not during the mating season. In some species the male and female exchange sounds and even perform duets during courtship. Some ornithologists believe that the pair is "discussing" the nesting site and that each individual is giving an opinion as to its suitability.

Song is more important in the life of a bird during the height of the mating season than at any other time. Some birds spend as much as eight or ten hours each day singing. As long as the male is unmated, he repeats his call over and over again, hour after hour. The champion caller recorded thus far may be the red-eyed vireo, who repeats his song well over 20,000 times a day until mating takes place.

The mating call is commonly species specific, conveying several meanings to other birds of the singer's species. It informs them that the caller is a male of their particular species; that he claims the territory in which he sings; that he is located at a particular place within his territory; and that he will defend his position if necessary. Evidence exists that not all birds use mating calls: crows, hawks, and some of the other large birds probably win mates by domination and through combat with rival males.

Alarm and distress cries or calls often are closely related. When seized by a predator, a bird gives a cry of distress, which in turn may serve as a danger signal or warning to other members of the flock. Many birds emit an explosive, piercing cry of alarm, which sometimes startles the predator into dropping its prey and brings fellow members of the victim's flock hurrying to the scene. Soon a din of alarm cries arises, and the intruder is attacked or driven away.

Ordinarily an alarm call causes birds to leave the area in which the call is given. But sometimes they may first approach the source of the call, then leave—as in the case of the herring gull. In their study *Pest Control with Sound*, Hubert and Mable Frings came up with the ingenious idea of recording distress calls of starlings and playing them back in areas where the birds had become a nuisance, thus causing them to fly away. To be effective the calls must be broadcast over an extended period. Even when the birds learn that danger is not imminent, they react instinctively to the distress call. However, the calls must not be broadcast for too long at a time, or repetition becomes abnormal and the birds learn that the calls are fake. The Fringes discovered that food-finding calls proved to be effective in dispersing laughing gulls after they had become accustomed and no longer responded to an alarm call.

Alarm calls often are specific in locating an intruder. When danger threatens overhead, blackbirds produce a long *seeee* sound; when the predator is on the ground, a *chuck* sound is repeated over and over again. Chickens also use two calls to convey this type of information. One call—described by Oskar and Katharina Heinroth in their book *The Birds* as having the sound *gogogogock*—is given when a ground predator is sighted; another—which the Heinroths describe as *rehh*—signifies that the enemy is airborne.

Some birdcalls are interspecific. The alarm calls of one species, for example, may elicit an appropriate response in an entirely different species. In his book *Bird-Song* W. H. Thorpe points out that a chaffinch and a blackbird produce almost identical calls when either sights a flying hawk. Certain bird-calls may even provoke a response from other animals. The African honey guide is a good example. The honey guide eats beeswax; but usually the bird cannot get it out of the hollow trees inhabited by bee colonies. By repeatedly approaching a small, weasel-like animal, the ratel, or else a man, then vocalizing and flying toward the bee tree, the honey guide leads the ratel or man to the honey source. When the honeycombs have been removed by ratel or man, the honey guide feasts on the wax that remains.

There are two general types of food calls: the call *to* food and the call *for* food, or begging call. The former is known to be given by only a few species of birds, and then only when the food is particularly abundant. Upon discovering a small quantity of food, a gull chokes it down quickly and quietly; but if there is more food than the bird can eat at one sitting, the feeding call is given. The American robin gives a food call that is answered by the nestlings; they reinforce their vocalizing with gaping beaks as a visual signal that they are ready for food. The *tek, tek, tek* of a rooster calling hens to a morsel of food is familiar to anyone who has spent time on a farm. When foraging adult penguins return with food and call to their young, the chicks always recognize the call of

George Purvis

Birds within a flock of a single species often are able to recognize each other because of individual variations in the overall pattern of song.

their parents from among those of thousands of penguins in the colony—even when the adults are packed closely together and seem all to be calling at the same time. Each pair of penguins utters its calls in rhythmic patterns; the patterns are distinctive for each pair. After the young have hatched, the parents give their food call over and over in the presence of their chicks for a period of several weeks, until the young have learned to recognize and distinguish it from all the others.

When the herring gull has found or captured a large amount of food, it often sounds a loud call that brings other gulls to join in the feast.

Young nestling birds usually beg for food by using calls of extremely low amplitude. The direction of these sounds is difficult to pinpoint, and many are so high pitched that they are virtually inaudible to the human ear. A parent bird, however, detects these sounds with ease from a distance of many yards. Probably a predatory bird, such as a hawk, has difficulty in locating the begging calls of these nestlings. Noisy rooks and ravens live in large, well-defended colonies; the only other noise-making nesters are those (such as woodpeckers) that raise young in protected holes.

Birds have a number of calls whose purpose is keeping the group together: calls of the mother to her young, flocking calls, flight calls, assembly calls, and a few others. Virtually all flocking birds have a flight call. When a flock of geese prepares to leave a site, these calls begin—softly at first, but becoming louder and increasing in tempo as takeoff time draws near. Finally a few geese begin to shake their heads from side to side in the signal of departure. As more and more head shaking occurs, the graceful, long-necked birds begin to skim over the water and lift easily into the air.

The female mallard duck gives her familiar soft quacks of "togetherness" the year round, except during the spring breeding season. Her *wark, wark, wark* as she leads her line of ducklings along is normally given very softly, but rises in pitch and intensity if danger threatens. During the breeding period, however, she waddles along silently with her mate. If a strange drake has the temerity to approach, she informs her mate immediately with urgent *qweg, qweg* sounds, while indicating the outsider with her bill. Usually the mate drives the stranger away promptly, attacking him if necessary.

At a brood site, parent graylag geese give their well-known *kagangak* calls to summon the goslings. Literally hundreds of graylags may be packed close together in a relatively small area; but the goslings know and respond to their parents' call, ignoring the many others that fill the air at the same time.

Frequently heard is the "mobbing," or assembly, call of

Nestling birds beg for food with high-pitched sounds that are frequently inaudible to the human ear. These calls are easily detected by the parent birds over long distances.

crows. If a lone crow spies an owl, it gives this raucous call, and all the other crows in the vicinity hurry over to join in a mass attack on their natural enemy. The effectiveness of this signal can be demonstrated by using a stuffed or imitation owl and an artificial crow call; recordings of crow calls played through portable loudspeakers produce even better results. Recorded alarm calls cause crows to disperse quickly, as the Fringses discovered in their experimental work. Writing in *Scientific American* ("The Language of Crows"), they tell how they substituted recordings of American crow calls for similar recordings of French crows. They found that although 50 percent of the French crows gathered at the sound of the American crows' assembly calls, no French crows responded to the American crows' alarm calls.

In the spring many birds stake out a claim to a territory, which they proceed to defend with all the strength and bluff they can muster. No bird tolerates the presence of another bird within the same territory. In most cases the territory automatically belongs to the first arrival. A weak and much-harassed gull, for example, may select a niche in a cliffside as his nesting site. At the approach of a second gull—even if it is a strong bird that has habitually pecked and otherwise dominated the nester—the weaker bird opens his beak, raises his wings, and screams. The latecomer always respects the property rights of the nester and leaves.

Territories serve various purposes: mating, nesting, feeding, roosting, and wintering. Nesting territories sometimes include only the immediate area around the nest, but often take in an appreciable amount of air and ground space. The male bird usually takes on the chore of defending the territory. He arrives at the general nesting area before the female, and has the territory established when she flies in a few days later.

Chasing, assuming threatening postures, vocalizing, and actual fighting are all used at one time or another by various birds during territorial defense; but vocalizing, usually in presentation of a territorial defense song, is used more often than any single other method. Some of the sparrows and robins in particular have songs of this type, and most birds are thought to have at least one cry of aggression in their repertoire. The *chaa*'s and *chu*'s of the buntings and certain finches probably signal aggression. Blackbirds defend their territories by means of the well-known "chinking" call, especially when other birds seek to invade their roosting trees. Variations of the chinking vocalization are used by virtually all birds as a cry of aggression; even the nonsinging birds almost always have such territorial defense calls.

Bird songs concerned with establishing and maintaining a territory are characteristically performed at greater volume than other types of songs. The threat of the singer must be made clear if potential intruders are to heed its implications. A territorial song usually is not sung separately but is rather a component of the basic song performed at this time of the year. The mating call is also integrated into this song; and other components enable the listener to determine quickly and accurately the direction of the song's source.

Innate and Acquired Calls

Efforts have been made to discover whether the ability of a bird to sing is innate or acquired. In those bird species tested, it has been found that certain components of bird songs are learned and other components inborn. The testing procedure is simple: Birds are hatched in the laboratory and reared in isolation. The song these birds sing at maturity are then compared with the songs of birds in the wild.

All bird songs include an inherited or inborn portion together with a portion that is learned from the mature members of the species in the wild. In addition, certain parts of the song are neither totally inherited nor learned from associates; these components are acquired through the great ability of the bird to imitate random sounds overheard.

Unless birds hear the sounds for which they have an innate aptitude, they never make them. This has been well established by allowing isolated birds to hear the complete song of nonisolated birds, either by capturing and bringing in wild birds or by means of recordings. On the other hand, the brush turkeys of Australia and a few other species of birds that hatch alone and grow up without ever seeing their parents do no calling of any kind.

What role does imitation of others play in the development of the complete song of a bird? More particularly, why does the bird—with a few exceptions, notably the mockingbird—imitate only the sounds of his own kind and not those of other species? Certain finches, for example, can be induced by artificial means (such as human whistling or playing on a bird pipe or flageolet) to make sounds. But artificial songs with very pure tones are not readily learned by most birds; neither are recorded songs of different species.

Mynahs, parrots, crows, and even canaries have vocal apparatus that can imitate the words of human speech with startling accuracy. Parakeets have been known to recite poetry, and pigeons to count up to six. But mere imitation of sound does not imply understanding or the ability to use "talk" to achieve a practical purpose. Mockingbirds, magpies, starlings, and various other songbirds are adept at mimicry; but even though they sing other birds' songs in addition to their own, these imitated sounds are produced independently of their own song and have no significance in the vocabulary of the species.

Other Types of Auditory Signals

Not all sounds produced by birds are vocalizations. In the spring the male ruffled grouse, for example, perches on a hollow stump or log and produces a drumming noise by rapidly and vigorously fanning his wings. This drumming serves the dual purpose of attracting a mate and warning off rivals.

Both the wing feathers and the tail feathers of birds may be modified for noise making. During courtship, for instance, one of the tropical manakins snaps certain feathers together like castanets. Some ducks as well as certain Australian goldeneyes and pigeons produce wing whistles. Undisputed king of the wing whistlers is the mute swan. Making a sound loud enough to be heard over long distances, he and his fellows keep in touch as they fly. This swan apparently does not have special feathers enabling him to produce his flight sound; the exact mechanism originating the whistle is not known.

Visual Signals

Instead of relying upon song for identification, many individual birds may distinguish each other by sight. In this form of recognition, body position, action, and coloration serve as visual signals. Responses of birds to visual signals often can be elicited experimentally by means of unsophisticated stimuli. German naturalist Konrad Z. Lorenz, for example, found that jackdaws attacked him when he carried a black cloth and allowed it to flutter about; if he persisted in this activity, the birds came to regard him as an enemy and attacked him even when he did not carry the cloth.

Birds sometimes perform highly stereotyped threat displays instead of giving threat calls. The American robin does not vocally threaten a trespasser; instead it runs toward the newcomer with lowered head, pausing now and then to assess the effect of the charge. Again rival male yellowtails approach within inches of each other, stand still, and lean far backward, bracing themselves with their tails. Then they begin a sidewise swaying motion, followed by clawing and pecking. Among herring gulls, when an outsider enters a gull's territory, the resident approaches, stops, and pulls up a large wad of grass with his beak. If the intruder accepts the challenge, he too pulls up a bunch of grass. At first each gull tries to dislodge the grass from the other's bill; but they inevitably end up grabbing wings and scuffling about.

Usually a bird drives away the males (only rarely females) of the same species when defending a territory, ignoring those of other species. The threat display of a mother goose is highly effective in driving an enemy away from her goslings. With feathers ruffled to present a more menacing appearance, the goose utters loud hissing noises. The gander, on the other hand, gives its famous honk at the first sign of danger. If the

During the mating season the sea-dwelling albatross gathers in groups on islands to breed. During their courtship the males and females dance about each other in pairs, bills pointed in the air.

goose is nearby, she heads for water, taking with her any goslings she may have.

One of the most rudimentary courtship displays is the feeding or mock feeding of the female by the male, found in the English robin, rook, crossbill, and certain other species. Where the sexes are similar in appearance, both play a major role in the courtship ceremony. When she enters the male's territory, the female identifies herself by adopting a submissive posture to help allay his aggression. Imitating a hungry nestling, she begs for food, which may then actually or in mimicry pass from mouth to mouth.

In a relatively few species of birds there is no apparent difference as to size, color, and so on between the sexes. The little Adélie penguin of the Antarctic coastal areas uses a testing procedure at courting time. Taking a small stone in his beak, a male penguin waddles up to another penguin and drops the stone. The second penguin, if a male, replies by attacking the pebble dropper; if an unreceptive female, by disdaining the proffered pebble; if a receptive female, by accepting the pebble—and the courtship begins.

Many birds have elaborate, ritualistic courtship patterns, often strikingly similar to those of fish. The displays involved are primarily visual, but are frequently auditory as well and sometimes even tactile. Even when the sex of the male bird is announced in song, his plumage is his badge of sex. Sometimes the shape or pattern of the plumage, sometimes the vivid colors, often both pattern and color, make up the badge. Crowns and crests of feathers on the head, plumes on the head and tail, and "bibs" on the chest are all types of specialized plumage used during courtship display. A male with specially colored or otherwise modified plumage loses no time in displaying his decorative features in the most direct and conspicuous manner. A peacock approaches a hen with the drab side of his fanned-out plumage toward her. When at a certain distance from the hen, he pivots and dramatically flashes the decorated side of his plumage in all its spendor, augmenting the action with an explosive *heah!*

One moment frenzied, the next with plumes quivering, then still, the male Count Salvadori bird of paradise displays himself before mating with a female. Such displays, which seem to stimulate both male and female to sexual readiness, are often carried out concertedly by large groups of these birds, the mass excitement perhaps heightening the stimulation.

Male sage grouse of the Western plains gather each season in communal display areas, called booming grounds, to perform their spectacular courting dances. These dances are actually dominance contests to establish mating priorities. Sometimes more than fifty cocks go through their paces together—tails fanned out, tips of stiffly held wings touching the ground, and orange neck pouches first inflated and then suddenly deflated to produce a booming noise. The admiring females try to select their mates from among the strutting performers, although approximately 80 percent of the mate selection is done by the dominant male. The dance of the sage grouse, with its bowing, strutting, and stamping, is mimicked in tribal dances by the Indians of the Northwest.

Some birds literally "flip" during their courtship antics. The male of one of the bird-of-paradise species, for example, falls backward off a branch, performs a complete somersault, and lands upright on the forest floor without so much as opening his tightly folded wings. The blue bird of paradise sings and displays his beautiful coloration while swinging upside down from a limb.

Penguins point their beaks far upward in the so-called posture of ecstacy, bow deeply in Oriental fashion, entwine their short necks as much as possible, and emit bugling sounds. Great crested grebes perform a similar "penguin dance" on water. Treading water furiously, both birds rise vertically and face each other, then present bits of water weeds held in the beak while weaving about in an almost snakelike manner.

Certain species of birds do their courting in the air. Some of the woodpeckers, herons, snipes, hawks, hummingbirds, swifts, and doves, for instance, carry out breathtaking aerobatics—diving and spinning from great heights with apparent unconcern and recklessness. Swifts have been known to come together in flight and drop for a thousand feet or more, locked in an embrace.

From what we have discovered about communication in birds, it is apparent that the calls, songs, visual displays, and so on relay relatively rudimentary information concerned mainly with the survival of the species, and that the birds' reaction to this information is instinctive for the most part. Although certain species are capable of imitating nonspecific sounds—even the sound of the human voice—there is no evidence to date that birds can learn to use new systems of communication to achieve practical purposes.

6. Land Mammals

Compared with what is known about certain members of the animal kingdom—birds, bees, and dolphins, for example —surprisingly little is known of communication in the non-primate land mammals. The reasons for this neglect are clear. For one thing, wild animals simply are not so visible as are birds and bees; they are usually nocturnal and tend to be secretive. Generally they are more numerous than birds, although the mammal populations fluctuate from one region to another. While the human eye may not readily detect them, as many as 200 mice, shrews, or other species of small mammals may inhabit an acre of meadow or woodland. A small mouse can exist on one-tenth of an acre, whereas a member of the deer family may require up to forty acres for survival.

Another reason for our relative ignorance of mammalian behavior is the inherent mobility of these animals. Many land mammals are nomads, at least for much of the year. Even though some travel in groups (packs of wolves and herds of deer, for instance), where communication is essential, many are solitary and may not encounter another of their species except for brief periods during the breeding season.

Finally, the only way to study these animals is in the field, for in captivity they do not reveal normal patterns of behavior —of which communication is one. Because field studies are expensive, time-consuming, and physically demanding, scientists often are reluctant to spend the months, or even years, necessary to conduct them.

Sufficient observational and experimental work has been done, however, to indicate that nonprimate land mammals possess a rich vocabulary of sign stimuli, or signals, that release a reaction in the animal or animals perceiving them. These signals serve well-defined functions within each species and are recognized by all its members.

Most land mammals have excellent senses of sight, smell, and hearing; many have acute senses of taste and touch. Each eye is equipped with focusing lenses, and a larynx serves as a sound box in vocalizations. Most mammals have three bones in the middle ear, and most also possess external ears. Many of these animals, including cats, dogs, deer, and horses, are provided with muscles that can raise or turn the ears to pick up and find the direction of sound-wave vibrations.

The sensitivity of the sense organs varies from species to species, depending upon the structure of the organ, the biological environment, and the behavioral patterns of the species. The rabbit depends on its three-inch-long ears and bulging eyes to detect sounds and sights from the rear as well as from the front and sides. The bear has less need for keen vision but relies to a great extent on the senses of smell and hearing. The burrowing mole, as well as many nocturnal mammals, has even less need for good vision or even good hearing, making its way in life with well-developed senses of smell and touch. For an animal as well protected as the porcupine, only a food-detecting olfactory sense is required.

Chemical Signals

In the lives of most mammals the sense of smell plays a dominant role. The use of scent is widespread—for example, in locating food, detecting the presence of enemies, marking and defending territorial boundaries, and bringing male and female together for mating. Scent glands in the face, feet, back, or anal region give many mammals a characteristic odor, which may serve as an attractant to other members of the species or as a repellent to an intruder or a predator.

To insure a safe feeding and breeding place for themselves, mammals often establish a home territory. Because meat eaters need wide areas for hunting, their families are spaced farther apart than are those of the plant eaters. The home range is crisscrossed by an elaborate network of trails or tracks connecting water holes, wallows, rubbing trees, dung pits, and other frequented spots; the "signposts" serving as its boundary markers are the animal's scent secretions or its urine and feces.

Bears mark trees by sticking some of their body hairs to the tree with mud. First the mud is smeared on the tree; then the bear scrapes his back several times against the muddy spot, applying enough pressure so that the rough tree bark pulls out a few hairs. This mark carries the body smell of the bear and probably conveys a good deal of information about its size and sex to another passing bear. A female examining this sign may elect to remain in the vicinity, especially if breeding time is approaching and if the bear that made the sign was a male. A male, on the other hand, may feel that one male in the area is enough, and move on to unmarked territory. All bear markings are probably made by males.

In another kind of sign language, a bear standing on his hind legs reaches up on a tree and makes deep scratches with his teeth and claws in the bark. The next bear to come by sniffs the tree, looks at the marks, and tries to scratch higher up. Failing in this effort, the bear may move on to find a territory where he can make the highest tree marks. By the same token, any bear already residing in this area may leave if he discovers higher marks than his, made by the newcomer.

Beavers mark the hillocks of mud or projecting objects that constitute their "signposts" with secretions from their castors, or musk glands. Badgers deposit a strong-smelling substance (called setting scent) secreted by their musk glands on paths and on the bases of trees and shrubs. The resulting scent trail indicates the boundaries of a territory—approximately four or five square miles of woodland—that is shared by one to three pairs of badgers. Antelope and red deer mark the ground, trees, and bushes with secretions from glands near their eyes; while the muntjac, a small deer of south-eastern Asia, uses the glands on its feet for marking. The California ground squirrel marks stones with scent from glands on its back. The droppings of the river otter, found at places where the animal rolls, dries off and deposits scent from its anal glands on tufts of grass, alert other otters passing through the area.

Mammals are continually sniffing the droppings of other mammals, particularly those of their species. From examination of these droppings an animal learns something about the size and sex of the producer and about what food is available in the area. When an unleashed dog goes for a jaunt around the neighborhood, he sniffs busily for places where dogs have been before him. Arriving at a spot that another dog has marked with urine, he sniffs carefully, then reacts usually in one of three ways: If he scratches the ground vigorously with his hind legs and growls, he has smelled the mark of a male —one he believes to be a potential challenger. If he whines and, after more sniffing, trots away, the scent mark was left by a female. If he trots away without either whining or scratching, he considers the mark unimportant—probably that of a smaller male, or at least of one with which he is familiar and which he knows poses no threat.

Scent is used in courtship to attract a mate and also as a sign of possession. Scent announces the sex of the sender and conveys information as to the sender's readiness to mate. The female weasel signifies her readiness by depositing a strong scent on the ground and vegetation as she moves along. The first male to encounter these deposits promptly leaves scent of his own, to discourage other males and to tell the female that he is in the vicinity.

In the early fall, buck deer make what is known as a scent pit or wallow. The buck leaves his scent in the pit by depositing urine and secretions from his scent glands. As in the weasel, this serves the purpose of attracting a female to the area or of driving away a potential challenger.

Some mammals discharge repellent odors, or musks (many of which are used as a base for perfume), when alarmed or as a defensive measure. In time of danger or as a warning to the rest of the herd, the collared peccary discharges musk from scent glands located near its short, invisible tail. The odor is also used for marking bushes and shrubs. It can be perceived by man from a distance of several hundred feet. The pronghorn discharges musk that can be scented from a distance of up to 500 yards. When the herd has been alerted, it gathers at a central point, and all members take off together.

Like other members of the weasel family, the wolverine has scent glands from which it emits a strong musk when angered. The musk is also sprayed on food, despoiling it to prevent other animals from taking it. This habit prompted Canadian Indians to give to the wolverine the nickname "skunk-bear."

But it is among the skunks themselves that the pheromone, or chemical signal, reaches its greatest development. The scent glands of the skunk produce about one-third of a liquid ounce per week of amber-colored musk—sufficient for about five consecutive discharges. Through ducts controlling two glands under its tail the skunk discharges the scent, usually in a fine spray, so accurately that it reaches an enemy's eyes at distances of up to eight feet. To some animals (and humans) the musk, which is composed of mercaptan, a sulfurous compound, is nauseous and may cause vomiting. It may also burn the eyes, causing temporary blindness. Skunks use scent as a defensive weapon only as a last resort, and never when fighting among themselves nor without ample visual and auditory warning to others.

Tactile Signals

Among mammals, courtship is strongly tactile and visual. Males and females of most species of deer, for example, come together to form herds only during the rutting season. At this time, males indulge in ritualized fighting to establish dominance and to induce females to gather around for mating.

American Museum of Natural History
Two bull elk fighting over the cows in the herd. The winner
will mate with the harem.

In this way the qualities of the strongest members of the
herd are passed on to future generations.

During the breeding season rival bull elk fill the frosty fall
air with bugled challenges and the crashing of antlers as they
meet in head-on contests for the favors of the cows. A pushing and shoving struggle then ensues, as each animal tries to
throw the other off balance. In similar fights between rutting
moose, their wide, palmate antlers sometimes become locked
together, and the animals die of starvation. Bighorn sheep
become extremely unsociable during the breeding season,
when the rams fight one another for mates. Two rival rams
stand side by side, then suddenly walk away in opposite directions. When about thirty or forty feet apart, they whirl around
and rear up on their hind legs. Dropping to all fours, they
rush toward each other with the speed of an express train,

Buck hares often fight over does in heat. The bucks stand on their hind legs and box each other with their forefeet until one is defeated and leaves the scene of combat. Often the fluffy fur scattered about after such a battle is used by local birds in building their nests.

and meet head on with apparently skull-shattering force. The rams, however, are merely dazed, and they continue the contest until one or both call it quits. The winner gathers together his small herd of ewes, which he must then defend against all challengers.

Battles between contending male hares in the spring are bloody and sometimes lethal. With ears laid back, the animals box with their front paws and kick each other with their hind feet, while their long claws make deep, raking cuts. The expression "mad as a March hare" is hardly exaggerated as a description of these courtship goings-on.

Instead of fighting, marmots sometimes engage in playful

courtship dances. One animal extends an invitation by tapping the other on the shoulder. The two dance nose to nose, fore-paws together, in an upright posture. Suddenly they push away, arching backward, then swing upright into place and knock their teeth together.

Gestures, caresses, and even kisses are all found among the courtship rituals of nonprimate mammals. Horses, cattle, and deer indulge in licking, nuzzling, neck rubbing, and butting head to head or head to flank. Elephants trumpet and entwine their trunks. Much of this activity occurs even outside the mating season. Giraffes, for example, often touch noses and rub their heads together. By way of greeting, many members of the cat family (even tigers) nuzzle one another and rub

American Museum of Natural History
Among mammals courtship is strongly tactile and visual. Here a zebra nuzzles another at the neck.

one another's head, neck, and body in a slow, leisurely manner. Prairie dog pups spend a great deal of time being groomed by members of their group. When one prairie dog adult identifies another as belonging to the same group, the two may groom each other, one animal rolling over onto its back and presenting its underside to the other.

Tactile signals may be associated with a general bond-forming behavior. Such signals may be used by the female, to keep the male at hand until she is ready to mate; by the parent, to hold the offspring until the training period is completed; or by members of a group, to keep the group together as a unit.

Visual Signals

Where mammals live in herds or similar aggregations, species recognition is by scent, by sight, or (usually) by a combination of the two. All animals have a definite body shape, and many develop specific colors; both these elements may act as visual signals. Most vertebrates have highly developed visual organs, which allow for distinctions not only between dark and light but also between shapes and, often, between colors. These animals tend to use such organs for communication at relatively short range.

Many mammals use facial expressions—which are simply rearrangements of form and color—to display emotions. Raccoons have unusually expressive faces and make amusing pets. They often imitate one another's facial expressions. For example, a coon may curl up its nose and stick out its tongue in a very human manner when smelling something disagreeable, and other members of the family that happen to be watching are likely to imitate the grimace.

Different attitudes of the head, ears, and tail have definite meanings, many of which are associated with the rank of the individual in the social hierarchy or with agonistic behavior, which includes aggressive and defensive fighting, escape attempts, and submission. In many instances the threat sequence of warning attitudes or bluffs plays a more important part than does actual fighting. A wolf, for example, displays its fangs, flattens its ears against its head, growls, and stares intently at an enemy. The stare in itself is considered a threat almost universally in the animal kingdom.

It is interesting to observe, for what it tells us about their rank and attitudes, what happens when two dogs meet. If the dogs are strangers, their hackles rise, and they walk stiff-legged until they are within sniffing distance of each other. Tails held upright, ears flattened, both animals then emit deep-throated growls. As they slowly circle each other, one dog may wag his tail slowly as a sign of dominance. Usually this induces tail wagging in the other, and the two trot off together or go their separate ways. On the other hand, the first dog may curl his upper lip, electing to fight; and the second animal either fights or puts its tail between its legs and cowers, or runs.

A fight is often avoided when one animal gives up and assumes a characteristic posture of submission. This may involve offering a vulnerable part of its body to the victor. When its life is in danger, for instance, a dog stands perfectly still, tail and hackles down, head raised so that the throat is exposed to attack. The victor always honors this act of submission. After waiting to make certain that the loser is not going to move, the victor urinates on any nearby upright object. This is an act of dismissal and the loser then departs hurriedly. In any later encounter the loser signals disavowal of aggressive feelings by running away or by lowering and wagging the tail.

Sometimes a solitary wolf, encountering a strange pack in the wild, tries to become a member—adopting a submissive attitude, wagging its tail, rolling on the ground, and making playful, puppylike gestures. After a few nips, the pack wolves usually allow the newcomer to join them; but occasionally they launch a vicious attack that ends in the newcomer's flight or death.

Alternation of aggression and submission also marks boundary encounters between prairie dogs from different groups. Each group knows the boundaries of its territory within a prairie dog township, and each member of a group

This is the violent climax of a battle between two young Arab
stallions for supremacy over their herd. Unlike the wrestling
snakes (page 60), these beasts bite and kick each other; such
fights often end with one animal dead or crippled.

has a ritual for challenging an animal from another group that intrudes in his territory. Crouched on their bellies and with tails raised, both animals creep toward each other. If they recognize each other as belonging to the same group, they "kiss" each other with lips open and teeth bared. If they are from different groups, each animals tries to bite the other's rump. Separating briefly, they continue the contest until one gives way and retreats.

Mammals usually take flight only when a predator—including man—approaches to within a so-called critical distance. This distance varies according to the species; within each species it varies with age, sex, and local conditions. If the predator takes off after the animal and gains on it, the pursued may suddenly change its tactics, abandon its flight, and take defensive action. Each species has developed its own defensive tactics and employs whatever weapons are available to it: teeth, claws, horns, antlers, quills, color, odor.

Some herd animals, such as musk oxen, enclose their young in a ring of adults when danger threatens. Others have an effective alarm system that may combine visual, auditory, and olfactory signals. Among deer, body position, head movements, ear twitching, color contrast, and flicking of the tail all play a part in communication. Many of us have had the good fortune to encounter a small herd of white-tailed deer in the woods. Alerted, one of the does—usually the oldest—turns and flashes the pure white underside of her twelve-inch tail as a danger signal. In an instant the other does vanish. Often the tail flasher gives a little bleat, reinforcing the visual signal. About midautumn each buck takes on the job of acting as sentinel to, and protector of, the doe he is following. He uses whistles, woofing sounds, and tail flashes to warn her of danger or of the approach of another buck. She sometimes also flashes her tail, but this is probably a direct, instinctive reaction to a danger stimulus rather than a response to his signal.

Little escapes the glance of the North American pronghorn, whose large black eyes with wide-angle vision provide it with the exceptional eyesight required to survive on the open prairies. When alarmed or frightened, the pronghorn raises its white rump hairs and turns them outward, nearly doubling the size of the visible area. When the sun is reflected from this so-called rosette, bright flashes can be seen for a distance of two miles.

Immobility also serves as a visual signal. The opossum is well versed in its art of "playing possum." When in danger this animal may lie on its side limply, feigning death, with its eyes closed, heartbeat slowed, and tongue lolling out of its mouth, and may even permit itself to be handled in this state. At other times it may bite anyone handling it or may take flight.

The porcupine, on the other hand, strikes a defensive attitude that should give any would-be predator pause. If an enemy approaches too closely, the porcupine turns its back, bends its nose under its body, and elevates the quills along its arched back, raising its tail slightly. Then lashing out with its tail, the animal leaves quills lodged painfully in its tormentor's face and body flesh.

The opossum's ability to discourage attackers by feigning death is so realistic that the phrase "playing possum" has long been a part of common speech.

A skunk always gives an enemy fair warning by arching its back and opening its mouth in a threatening manner. At the approach of a persistent intruder, the skunk lowers its head, growls, and fixes its foe with a direct stare, then stamps on the ground with its forefeet or rakes at the grass with its long claws. Finally, arching its tail over its back, the animal turns its body sideways in a U shape and discharges a pungent spray of musk from the anal scent glands. The spotted skunk adds to its threat display by performing a handstand, advancing on its forefeet against its foe with hindquarters and tail elevated.

Male elk and moose use auditory signals to attract females from a distance, but identify themselves and pay court by visual signals—gaits and postures. An almost aggressive spirit is evident in certain mammalian courtship displays. Male cats and horses, for example, may actually bite the females, though the latter do not seem to mind. A male dog never attacks a strange female of the species; he wags his tail and prances about to show her that he is friendly. She may try to ignore him or may nip and growl at him to drive him away. Or, after a short period of aloofness, she may decide to play. Like most mammals, she mates only when in estrus, or "heat."

Hectic chases mark the courtship of certain lagomorphs. During the mating season, which begins in March and may last a month, the male varying, or snowshoe, hare pursues the female up hill and down dale at speeds that may reach thirty miles per hour; sometimes the female leaps suddenly into the air and darts off in a new direction. The cottontail is also given to chases and sudden aerial leaps. The rutting male European rabbit frequently alternates chases with tail flagging, advancing stiff legged toward the female with tail laid flat along the back. Then, walking away from the female for a short distance, showing his white tail, the animal returns and repeats the process several times. On other occasions the European rabbit may parade stiff legged around the female, hindquarters turned toward her to keep his white tail in view; or he may simply parade up and down in front of her.

Some rodent and ungulate species also engage in prenuptial pursuit. The male roe deer, for example, pursues the female

American Museum of Natural History
A seal rookery on St. Paul Island in the Bering Sea. Note the
large bull and his harem in the center.

day and night, sometimes going round and round in circles.

Care of the young is usually much more elaborate among mammals than among lower orders of animals. At first the signals of parents to young tend to be chiefly tactile. When their eyes open, the young then respond to adult auditory and visual signals—but often in a different way from the adults. For example, fawns of a deer family react to an alarm signal not by taking flight but rather by "freezing": they flatten themselves against the ground so that their spotted coats merge with the dappled pattern of sunlight through the underbrush to create a perfect camouflage. With maturity the fawns react to adult signals in the adult way. The defense reactions of young animals against their natural predators are principally learned; the parents must "educate" their offspring by example. Otter parents cooperate in teaching their young to hunt, fish, and swim—in other words, to survive. George Schaller once watched an adult tigress knock down a buffalo without killing or seriously injuring it, then look on while her cubs tried to complete the kill. Before the buffalo was dead, however, the mother had to knock the animal down again for the lumbering, uncoordinated cubs.

A female skunk uses both visual and auditory signals to keep her young brood in line. At the first hint of danger the mother points her nose in the direction of the disturbance and becomes rigid. The half-dozen offspring comprising the brood immediately imitate her. If the mother elects to hide, she makes soft, twittering noises as she disappears into the underbrush, frequently looking back to make sure her brood is following. When no danger threatens, the female churrs and twitters to her offspring so that they always know where she is.

Often the young animal has to learn its relationship to other members of its group and society. The young prairie dog, for instance, spends much of his time being groomed by his family and by members of his own and neighboring groups. He is not attacked or rebuffed when he enters the territory of other groups. But as he matures all this changes, and his excursions meet with increasing hostility—especially when he fails to realize that his territorial call should not be uttered on someone else's territory. Through the agonistic postures and displays of neighbors, the prairie dog learns the limits of his home territory.

Auditory Signals

Sound is used by land mammals for communication over a distance. When used at close range, it is generally accompanied by a combination of other sensory signals. A dog's bark, for instance, may indicate fear, threat, alarm, excitement, or similar emotion. The motions of a dog's body and tail are important in his repertory of signals, as we know. When barking and body motions are used simultaneously, this mixture of visual and auditory signals can be confusing to human beings. One day my small daughter came running into the house and breathlessly exclaimed that there was a strange dog in our yard. "Did he bark at you or was he wagging his tail?" I asked. "He was doing both," was the reply, "and I didn't know which end to believe."

Sounds that accompany aggressive or threatening postures are not required to carry over distances and thus are generally low-pitched. Raccoons, for example, growl and raise their tails and their body hair in the manner of a dog when they are trying to intimidate each other. Bears have their growls of anger and threat; but the sound to be wary of is the bear's cough. When a bear emits his coughing sound, he is about to attack a foe—perhaps another bear, or even a man. Coughs often prevent actual physical battle between bears, because the animal with the most ferocious-sounding cough can bluff his opponent into retreating. Bears also have their repertory of snarling grimaces, similar to those seen in other mammalian threat displays.

Virtually all members of the cat family employ warning and threatening signals, such as growls and hisses, accompanied usually by arching of the back and erection of the hair on tail and body. They also spit and snarl in anger. Although tigers try to avoid close contact with man, like the bear they cough or give a coughing roar as a warning if annoyed or angry.

The weasel hisses in warning and snarls or growls as a threat. The threat sound of the river otter, the weasel's close relative, is a peculiar combination of whistle and squeal. Skunks do not use their scent when fighting one another; instead they growl, bite, stamp their feet, and stare.

Auditory signals are commonly employed by land mammals to claim and maintain territorial boundaries. Such signals are used with much greater frequency, however, by animals that settle in one place (such as prairie dogs) than by such nomadic animals as sheep and deer.

Prairie dogs live in burrows, which together form "townships" that often cover several acres. Around each of the burrow's several openings is a mound of earth dug out by the animals to keep water from entering and flooding the burrow. From this raised vantage point the prairie dog surveys his surroundings and communicates signals of both danger and ownership. Each group of prairie dogs knows the boundaries of its territory within the township and learns to distinguish members of the same group from those of other groups. Sometimes the plump little sentinel gives his territorial call so forcibly that he jumps into the air or even falls over backward.

On the mound at the entrance to his burrow the prairie dog sits upright, in order to see as far as possible. At the approach of danger he scurries into his home burrow or into the nearest hole. If the danger is not immediate, he sits at the entrance of the burrow or peeps out, uttering a sharp chirp that resembles a bark—hence the derivation of the animal's name. The prairie dog uses various alarm calls, depending on whether the enemy is approaching on the ground or from the air.

Marmots perch on rocky lookouts to detect approaching danger, which (when immediate) is announced by a shrill, piercing whistle. From this call is derived the French-Canadian trappers' name for the hoary marmot of the Rockies: *le siffleur*, the whistler. At the whistled signal all marmots in a colony drop out of sight. They reappear when the all-clear signal—a low whistle—indicates that the danger has passed. Two other members of the marmot family, the yellow-bellied marmot and the woodchuck, are more nearly chirpers than whistlers.

Disagreement among squirrels is caused by contested territorial rights. These gregarious animals chatter and make churring noises to proclaim their territories. Some of these territories are staked out only for food-gathering purposes. The red squirrel, for instance, scolds, whistles, and shrieks in defense of its food cache against others of its species.

Like birds, mammals often vary the intensity of vocalized signals to indicate high or low levels of alarm. The chirp of the adult California ground squirrel, for example, varies in pitch, inflection, and loudness according to the situation. Spying a bird of prey flying nearby, the squirrel utters an abrupt, loud *cheesk*, then takes cover; other squirrels join in the alarm call and duck into their holes. When the predator is a snake, the squirrel approaches it slowly, then stops, flicks its tail vigorously from side to side, and emits a peculiar vibrating *cheet'-ik-irr-irr-irr*—a chirp that begins on a loud, sharp note, followed by a series of lower-pitched notes. The tail-flicking and chirping attract the attention of other squirrels in the area. When the danger does not constitute an immediate hazard, a *cheesk-isk-isk-isk-isk* signal is given.

Mutual cooperation is frequently the rule where animals find it advantageous to share food sources. The hunting technique of a pair of coyotes in a prairie dog township illustrates graphically the subtle directive signals of the coyote, which usually involve the use of several senses. When the pair (often a male and female) come upon a prairie dog settlement, they stand perfectly still out of sight and watch for several minutes. One coyote—usually the male—turns to the other and looks at her; often they touch noses. The female then sits on her haunches while the male, yapping continuously, walks into the area of the burrows, and prairie dogs scramble for their holes. The female coyote watches a burrow into which a particularly fat rodent has vanished. The male coyote now gives a single loud yap, as a signal to his hunting partner; she moves quickly to the side of the selected burrow and crouches. The male resumes his yapping and passes on through the prairie dog township. As his voice fades away into the distance, the rodents start reappearing for a look around. When the fat one pops up, the female coyote grabs it.

During regular migrations by some species of mammals, such as the North American caribou, bats, and cetaceans, it is virtually certain that use is made of one or more forms of communication in order to maintain the cohesiveness or integrity of the group. Although they can see with their eyes, bats navigate by means of echo location, in using a built-in "sonar" (after the Navy's Sound Navigation and Ranging). In flight the bat emits sounds of such high frequency (up to 100,000 cycles per second) that they cannot be heard by the human ear. Only by recording the supersonic sounds on high-speed tape recorders and playing them back at slower speeds can their frequency be reduced to the range of human hearing. These supersonic sounds are uttered at a rate of thirty to sixty per second until they bounce off an object—usually no farther away than four or five yards—and are echoed back to the bat's tragus and ear. The echoes form a "picture" in the bat's brain, permitting it to "see" objects and avoid them, if necessary. Buzzing and clicking noises accompany the sonar sounds. Bats use sound waves in the same way to locate their prey. When the bat's large ears are plugged so that it cannot hear, the animal loses its ability to avoid objects and locate prey; the same is true when its mouth is plugged.

In their pioneering studies Doctors R. Galambos and D. R. Griffin of Harvard University found that at least four species —the little brown bat, the big brown bat, Keen's bat, and the eastern pipistrelle—also emit a shrill cry, of a frequency of 7,000 cycles per second, that continues for a quarter of a second and is audible to the human ear. It is possible that bats use auditory signals not only for navigation and food seeking but also for communication with one another.

Distress calls among the higher vertebrates bear a marked resemblance to one another, indicating that a source of danger to one group may also represent danger to other groups composed of animals of corresponding size. Although usually silent as adults, rabbits sometimes scream when in pain or in mortal danger. The distress calls of rats and mice are ultrasonic—pitched too high to be heard by the human ear. Because these rodents can also hear at least two octaves higher than man, they are able to respond to the calls. A frightened fawn makes a bleating sound like that of a lamb, but its cries are not always heeded. Dr. George Schaller once watched a tigress chasing an axis deer and her fawn. The big cat leaped upon the fawn, striking it down. Ignoring the bleating of her dying offspring, the doe immediately resumed grazing only a few yards away.

Mammals generally employ odors for sexual attraction and identification, but some—particularly the ungulates and members of the cat family—use sound. In late fall the bull elk can be heard bugling his mating call in the mountains of the northwestern United States as he rounds up his harem of cows. The call begins as a roar, rises in pitch until it sounds like a French horn, and climaxes as an explosive scream; it is punctuated by several deep grunting sounds at the end. In the Ouachita River bottoms, or swamplands, I have felt the hair on the back of my neck rise at the scream of a mountain lion in the night. The mating call of this big cat (also known as the cougar, the panther, or the "screamer") sounds like a woman or a child screaming in mortal terror.

Like certain insects and amphibians, coyotes sometimes congregate in small packs and sing in chorus. The song of the solitary coyote is probably a mating call, and the group effort may also serve to attract females. This pooling of sounds serves to increase the strength and effectiveness of the signal.

Even the tiny shrew has a courting procedure that includes vocalizations. The male makes almost continuous clickings as he excitedly pursues the female. If the latter is unreceptive, she announces this fact by uttering a series of squeaks. If the male persists in ignoring this warning, the female fends him off with a threatening, high-pitched chattering sound.

The mating call of the striped skunk is a cooing whistle, almost dovelike but higher in pitch. At the end it changes to a purring sound.

Directive sound signals are used in training the young; offspring of predatory mammals learn by listening to and imitating calls as they accompany their parents on nightly food forays. Predatory mammals raised in captivity by man have a hard time learning to hunt: they may not recognize a natural prey as a potential meal and have no idea how to stalk, capture, and kill it.

Wolf cubs whine and whimper like dogs when they are hungry or when their mother is absent too long from the den. If they become too loud or rowdy, the mother quiets them with a low-pitched growl. After weaning, the cubs are brought meat by one or both parents; finally, they are taught to hunt.

Baby raccoons often climb to the topmost branches of a tree. Then, unable to get down, they hang on and squeal for their mother to rescue them. Young weasels often make bird-like chirps and crowing sounds when at play, and whine when separated from their mothers. A mother weasel may coo to her offspring as a signal for them to stay close to her; when danger threatens, she screams a warning. When danger is not an immediate threat, a California ground squirrel mother with young repeats a low *chwert* at two- or three-second intervals as an expression of anxiety.

The river otter, a close relative of the weasel, provides an example of the importance of play in the social development of mammals. Groups of fun-loving otters slide down muddy riverbanks, the pups chuckling with delight and the adults chirping, chattering, and grunting as they romp. Bighorn lambs like to play a version of "king-of-the-mountain," gamboling about and dashing up to the tops of large boulders. Now and again several of the ewes join in the fun, and strenuous bleating fills the air.

In addition to vocalizations, land mammals produce a number of other sounds. These are employed chiefly as alarm signals. The porcupine, for instance, accentuates its grumbled warning by clicking its teeth. Pronghorn rams sometimes grind their teeth to express anger. The varying, or snowshoe, hare indicates danger by thumping with its hind feet, sometimes with the left foot and sometimes with the right. The fat-tailed gerbil and many other rodents also drum on the ground with their hind feet as an alarm signal, while the dusky-footed wood rat rattles its tail.

The beaver uses its scaley, horizontally flattened tail as a warning mechanism. It sounds an alarm by bringing the tail quickly up over its back, then down with such force on the surface of the water that the resulting *crack* can be heard for half a mile on a quiet night. Almost simultaneously with the *crack*, all the beavers in the vicinity dive. Muskrat and nutria use their rounded tails to slap the water in similar fashion when trouble is at hand.

Interspecific Communication

The sounds and other signals employed by a mammalian species are designed primarily for communication within that species. But often these signals—especially if they happen to be calls of alarm or danger, or even territorial displays—affect other species as well when the latter share the same breeding or feeding territories.

The alarm squeal of a rabbit brings coyotes, fox, and sometimes even deer and the ever-cautious wolf running toward the sound. In many parts of Africa water is scarce, and several species of mammals frequently are found sharing the same water hole. For example, waterbuck, wildebeest, and zebras, and perhaps several other species as well, may be drinking from the same water hole at the same time. In such an aggregation the zebra acts as sentinel for the group. With its extremely sensitive hearing and keen sense of smell, the zebra can often detect a predator, such as a stalking lion, much sooner than can the other animals and so is able to give an alarm in sufficient time for all to take flight.

In Florida, cattle egrets frequent the same places as cattle and alert their bovine companions to danger with their alarm calls. In similar fashion African rhino birds serve as sentinels for rhinoceros.

Sometimes the badger and the coyote join forces in a hunting partnership, but in this the clever coyote usually comes out ahead. When the coyote discovers a badger in the process of digging out a ground-burrowing rodent, he waits nearby, well aware that while the badger is busily occupied at one entrance to the burrow, the intended victim is likely to pop out of another. When the rodent does appear, the coyote often manages to seize it before it can reach the safety of another burrow. Unfortunately the badger never manages to share in the catch.

As far as we know, communication in the land mammals consists mostly of simple information about their emotional states—fear, anger, hunger, pain, and so on. But because they rely to a great extent upon sensory signals to which we cannot respond (odor, for example), our knowledge is largely conjecture. Far less is known about social communication in land mammals than, for example, in ants; in this field much progress remains to be made.

7. Aquatic Mammals

Recently marine scientists arranged a long-distance telephone conversation between a male dolphin in California and a female of the species in Florida. Each took turns chirping, squawking, grunting, squeaking, and listening politely to the other's remarks. The female, as it turned out, was the chattier of the two.

Although we have known for some time that the dolphin quickly learns to perform difficult tricks, only now are we beginning to understand that this animal has remarkable methods of communication. If this is so, what about the other aquatic mammals—the walrus, the horn-honking trained seal (as the California sea lion is erroneously called), the whale? After spending all-night vigils with a white whale named Namu, animal-film producer Ivan Tors reported that the five-ton mammal was "the most intelligent creature I ever met."

The pinnipeds— which include the true (or earless) seals, the sea lions and other eared seals, and the walrus—and the cetaceans—which include whales, porpoises, and dolphins—are mammals that live entirely in or near the water. In the distant past the aquatic mammals were land mammals, but all now have developed special physiological adaptations for life at sea. The flippers of present-day seals, for example, gradually replaced the feet and legs of their ancestors. This modification of their limbs hampers the pinnipeds, or "fin-footed ones," on land but helps them to move swiftly in the water. Aquatic mammals also have larger, longer lungs than do the terrestrial mammals. When these water-dwelling animals submerge, special muscles or valves contract to slow the flow of blood to the extremities while allowing it to flow freely to the heart and brain. The aquatic mammals also have ears and nostrils that close when under water.

Visual Signals

Marine mammals do not have particularly good eyesight, though it is better developed in the pinnipeds than in the cetaceans. Occasionally the sperm whale lifts its head out of the water to look about, and the bottle-nosed dolphin can see moving objects in the air at a distance of about forty feet. However, because their eyes are placed laterally—on the sides of the head rather than in front—cetaceans lack depth perception and stereoscopic sight. Their vision is further limited by the fact that ocean water is not highly transparent. The small eyes of whales, porpoises, and dolphins can withstand extreme pressure when the animals descend to great depths, and they are equipped with tear glands that produce an oily secretion acting as a protection against irritation by salt water.

Considering their limited eyesight, it is hardly surprising that the aquatic mammals do not communicate through visual signals to any marked degree. The hooded seal of both sexes has an inflatable hood or pouch of muscle tissue (larger in the male than in the female) that extends from the nose to the top of the head. When angered or otherwise aroused, the seal inflates the pouch, which turns a brilliant red, and lets out a roar that can be heard several miles away. This audio-visual display effectively frightens away any potential enemy. The bull elephant seal uses its eighteen-inch snout in the same way to scare off rivals during the mating season. Filling the snout with air until the tip curls into the mouth, the bull then releases the air suddenly to produce a deep, ventriloquial roar.

Aside from displays involved with territorial defense and mating, little is known about the visual signals of aquatic mammals.

Olfactory and Tactile Signals

The seals and walruses are much more gregarious than are the land carnivores with which they were formerly grouped. Only a few species are solitary. The majority (notably the eared seals) live in colonies called rookeries, whose population may number from 100 individuals to 1 million. It is possible that mutual identification of parents and young amid this melee is aided by the sense of smell. Although not especially well developed in pinnipeds, the olfactory sense is utilized by all young mammals to a much greater extent than is the visual sense.

Whales and dophins, on the other hand, have little or no sense of smell. The olfactory nerves are vestigial, and the olfactory bulbs—well developed in the brains of mammals with a keen sense of smell—are nonexistent. Although they have lungs and breathe air like other mammals, cetaceans cannot live on dry land. The air-breathing nostrils open externally through a blowhole (single in toothed whales, dolphins, and porpoises, and double in baleen whales), which usually is located at the highest point on the head. The lungs are connected directly with the blowhole, not with the mouth as in other mammals. Breathing occurs at widely spaced intervals and is synchronized with surfacing; the blowhole automatically closes when the animal submerges.

Cetaceans appear to have a keen sense of taste. It is possible that after locating a fish by means of sound, they make the final decision whether to eat it by first tasting the water nearby.

Tactile organs in the skin of aquatic mammals are numerous, and the sense of touch is well developed. The walrus and earless seals, for example, probably use their snout vibrissae, or whiskers, to locate food organisms along the muddy floor of the turbid ocean waters where they live.

The sense of touch is important also in the care of the young and in courtship. So zealously does the mother walrus defend and guard her young that she carries her small calf on her neck even when swimming and diving. A courting pair of Falkland sea lions often climb ashore and sit facing each other for hours on end, twisting their necks from side to side like snakes and caressing each other on the front and side of the neck and, occasionally, mouth to mouth. From time to time the female may gently nibble at the male's neck.

In the beginning, dolphin courtship is a gentle affair, consisting largely of the antics of the male as he shows off for his lady friend. After a while, however, the male decides to take action. Like a dart he flashes over the female's back, stroking her lightly with his flippers. Then quickly rolling on his back, he swims beneath her, pressing his flippers against hers in a fleeting moment of caress. Sometimes one or both

When the mother dolphin feels her baby nuzzling her side to nurse, she squirts her superrich milk directly into his mouth. Such instant nursing is necessary with a baby who must surface twice a minute to breathe.

parties indulge in a certain amount of nuzzling, and often there is nibbling of flippers, accompanied by gentle murmuring sounds and high-pitched whines.

Finally, becoming impatient, the male dolphin speeds toward the female head on, brushing his body against hers as a collision is narrowly avoided. Quickly falling into the spirit of things, the female races away, followed by the male, with both of them often making great leaps out of the water and vocalizing loudly as they do so.

In similar fashion, pairs of humpback whales swim side by side, exchanging occasional resounding blows with their flippers. Like the dolphins, they may throw themselves out of the water and fall back with a tremendous splash.

Auditory Signals

Like other mammals, marine mammals have internal ear structures, with three bones in the middle ear. From a tiny external ear opening, a hearing canal leads to the internal ear. The auditory nerve connects the hearing apparatus to the brain, permitting sounds to be interpreted by the animal. It also allows scientific brain-mapping experiments, such as have been performed with outstanding success in the case of the dolphin. In the brain-mapping procedure, the animal is anesthetized, and the cerebral cortex is stimulated by passing small electrodes into the brain at various points and applying a weak electrical stimulus. The dolphin is watched closely for evidence of response, including vocalizations. Brain areas concerned with hearing, vision, tactile sensation, body movements, and emotional responses frequently can be delimited in this way. Often the stimulus in a given area must be increased appreciably in order to elicit a response. In certain areas of the brain a relatively strong stimulus causes the dolphin to emit distress calls.

The eared seals are noisy animals, whereas the earless seals are comparatively quiet. During mating time the cows and pups in a colony of eared seals can be heard howling and bleating; but by far the loudest sounds are the barks and roars of the fully mature males. Within any rookery of eared seals there is an almost constant uproar created by these sounds, interspersed now and then with a peculiar squall made by a pup that has become separated from its mother.

In the spring the eared bulls stake out territories in a location where they expect to breed and declare with loud roars their intention to defend their territories. These animals are polygamous, often gathering a harem of cows ranging in number from 10 or 15, in the case of the Steller's sea lion, up to 100, in the case of the northern fur seal. The latter guards his harem jealously day and night—never leaving his property even long enough to seek food, and bellowing defiantly to protect both his females and his territory. The northern fur seal trusts neither his cows nor his neighbors. Sometimes two fur seal bulls actually clash; the battle ends when one bull bellows in pain and leaves the harem to the roaring, strutting victor.

Sea lion bulls are more tolerant. However, young male sea lions bellow and roar at one another even though they have no harem to defend. They seem to be preparing themselves for the day when they cease to be bachelors and can command their own territories. Female sea lions also vocalize, though their calls are of higher pitch and lower intensity than are those of the males. Some female vocalizations probably are associated with mating, others with care of the young.

The sounds of the true seals are confined largely to low growls, snorting, and blowing. These animals are promiscuous in their mating habits and do not congregate in large rookeries or gather large harems. The gray seal bull, for example, fights to protect his territorial rights but not for possession of the cows. The seals defend themselves by advancing on an interloper with mouth open, uttering menacing cries, or by fleeing to the water and diving in. At the end of the mating season, the mature bulls haul themselves up on the rocks to relax in the sunshine, bickering in noisy bellows over their favorite locations.

Young seals do not take to swimming automatically; they must be taught. The Weddell seal mother, for example, employs the familiar "come on in, the water's fine" routine. Fourteen days after the birth of her pup, the mother coaxes him into the water by plunging in herself and then calling him to join her. While the pup is working up his courage to face the ordeal, the mother seal scrapes out a ramp in the ice with her teeth so that he can slide safely into the water.

Several species of mammals demonstrate remarkable homing and direction-finding abilities. The harp seal, for example, frequents Arctic waters but reproduces in only three localities within its range: the White Sea, the western North Atlantic, and the vicinity of Newfoundland. Migrating singly or in small groups to its breeding places in the fall, the seal returns to more northerly latitudes in summer. The northern fur seal also travels to breeding rookeries, sometimes covering distances of almost 9,000 miles per year; and the California gray whale navigates 6,000 miles, mostly over open sea, in its yearly migrations from the Arctic Ocean and Bering Sea to the California coast and back.

Except for the short barks given by true seals to keep the members of the group within the same general areas, little is known concerning the methods of communication employed by migrating marine mammals. Professor E. J. Slijper states in his book *Whales* that schools of these cetaceans are probably kept intact by the use of sounds as a means of communication. It is also likely that when scattered in every direction by whale hunters, schools of whales reassemble by using sound signals to locate one another. For inexplicable reasons schools of whales sometimes commit mass suicide—as many as a hundred may beach themselves on the shore—perhaps using similar signals.

In the Antarctic a few years ago, a fishing fleet found that thousands of killer whales had arrived first at the fishing grounds and were busily eating and driving away the fishermen's quarry. One ship radioed a fleet of whaling vessels. Several whalers arrived; one shot was fired from a single harpoon gun. Minutes later not a whale could be seen within the fifty-square-mile area covered by the whaling ships—and none returned. Although only one whale had been hit, he most certainly had sounded distress or alarm calls. At any rate, information about the danger lurking on the surface of the sea must have passed rapidly through the herd.

The entire life of the whale is intimately bound up with his ability to perceive and produce sounds. He hears sounds made by the crustaceans on which he feeds and by his fellow whales when they cry out in distress. He also uses echo location—for securing food—bouncing sounds off submerged objects to determine their shape, size, distance. And many naturalists and fishermen have reported hearing whales whistle, squeal, and make similar noises.

Underwater recordings of cetacean sounds made by William E. Schevill and William A. Watkins at Woods Hole, Massachusetts, showed (when converted into sound spectrograms) that these animals use vocal sounds to convey definite meanings. Many other types of sounds were recorded, the greater number of them with knowledge of the circumstances under which they were made and, consequently, of their interpretive significance. Studies made with the use of hydrophones revealed that the utility of many sounds probably depended on echo location in locating and securing food, and that these sounds perhaps were also used for communication between individuals. The sperm whale, for example, was found to produce numerous sounds, variously described as consisting of "a series of sharp clicks," "a grating sort of groan, very low in pitch," "a rusty hinge creaking," and "a muffled smashing noise."

Sounds produced by the white whale, or beluga (a member of a dolphin-porpoise subfamily) were recorded by Schevill and Barbara Lawrence in the lower Saguenay River in Quebec. They found that this animal richly deserved its title "sea canary," with its varied vocabulary consisting of ticking and clucking sounds, mews, chirps, resonating high-pitched

Miami Seaquarium

Experts consider bottle-nosed dolphins to be quite intelligent. They not only are trained for shows at aquariums and zoos but also are the subject of many studies and experiments to measure their intelligence and communicate with them. Dolphins have a large and varied vocabulary, and are even able to mimic human speech.

whistles and squeals, bell-like sounds, and low trills. All these sounds are made in a key too high for the human ear to detect unaided; but occasionally schools of white whales produce sounds resembling a crowd of children shouting in the distance. Sound most likely is produced by emission of a stream of bubbles through the blowhole rather than by a voice box.

Man has long known that dolphins produce sounds and are affected by them. Aristotle claimed that dolphins, on being captured, moaned and made squeaking noises in the air. He also stated that dolphins quickly swam away from noises, and curiously he believed that they had no acoustic passageway.

Dolphins and porpoises are close relatives—so close that the names are sometimes used interchangeably. The term "porpoise" is correctly applied, however, only to those round-headed animals without beaks and with laterally compressed teeth. Dolphins have beaks and rather spikelike teeth. Both animals are highly intelligent and are favorites at various marinelands throughout the United States, where they are taught to retrieve a thrown ball or stick, to leap through hoops, and to perform a variety of similar tricks.

Most of what we know about dolphin communication comes from studies of the playful bottle-nosed dolphin (*Tursiops truncatus*). This animal weighs around 300 pounds and has a brain weighing about $3\frac{1}{2}$ pounds—the biggest brain for its size of all animals with the exception of man. The brain is deeply furrowed, convoluted, and highly developed. According to some experts dolphin intelligence ranks between that of the dog and that of the chimpanzee; others believe that the dolphin outranks even the chimpanzee.

In 1953 W. G. Wood, Jr., curator of Marineland at St. Augustine, Florida, identified six or seven of the various sounds used by dolphins to communicate with one another and for other purposes. The jaw clap—a flat, abrupt noise resembling clapping—indicates a threat or warning and is used by the eldest male in the group. A short flat whistle followed by a high-pitched, musical one is a distress call. Any other dolphins that happen to be within hearing distance reply to this call; when a mother dolphin whistles for her baby, for example, the baby whistles back. A barking sound can represent a warning or anger; it was recorded coming from an animal being pursued by a shark. Adult males sometimes emit a yelping sound like a puppy's which may be a mating call. Mewing and rasping sounds are made while feeding. The "rusty hinge" sound represents the dolphin's "sonar." This sound is produced by a series of rapidly pulsating clicks. The rate of clicking ranges from approximately half a dozen to over several hundred sounds per second. At an exceedingly high rate, these clicks can be detected by the human ear only with the aid of special equipment.

Among the other vocal sounds emitted by dolphins are chirps, grunts, squawks, and even sounds resembling those of the human voice. Probably only dolphins that have been closely associated with humans produce the loud singing sounds heard at the various oceanariums. Also, captive animals are more likely than free-ranging ones to emit sounds above water. Dr. John C. Lilly, one neurophysiologist who studied the dolphin brain, was so impressed by the sounds produced by these creatures that he determined to learn their meaning. In 1955 he built a laboratory for that purpose in the Virgin Islands. One day while testing a dolphin in a tank, he called to an assistant, "Three-two-three." From the tank came the unmistakable reply: "Three-two-three."

Dolphins have no vocal cords, and the problem of ascertaining their method of sound production has until recently been a difficult one. Researches lately conducted have demonstrated that deep inside the blowhole, in the nasal passageway, are two tonguelike projections or flaps that overlap like valves. Air blown through the nasal passageway causes the flaps to flutter, and noises result. Variations in pitch are probably brought about by the increasing and decreasing tension on the nasal flaps. In addition to the flaps there is also in the blowhole a maneuverable "tongue" or "plug." This and a similar mechanism deep inside the airway also aid in the production of sounds.

Dolphin noises are emitted in vibrations whose frequencies range from about 3,000 to 200,000—possibly even 300,000—

cycles per second. The noises resulting from extreme high-frequency vibrations are mostly putting and creaking sounds, and are essentially like some of those emitted at lower frequencies. The whistling noises so often heard in the vocalizations of dolphins are sometimes produced within the fairly low range of 6,000 to 16,000 cycles per second, each whistle lasting about one-half second. The limitations in the dolphin's vocal apparatus lend a "quacking" quality to the almost human sounds he so readily learns to make, but these sounds are wordlike nonetheless.

Dolphin "Sonar"

While carrying out a series of experiments with a dolphin at Nonomesset Island, Massachusetts, in 1958, William Schevill and Barbara Lawrence discovered that the animal could hear ultrasonic sounds in the 140-kilocycle range and could perceive objects by means of reflected sound. They also demonstrated that the dolphin uses its "rusty hinge" sound as an echo-locating or sonar device.

Among the recorded sounds of dolphins (especially in those recordings which have been slowed down for analysis), pings and resultant echoing pings are clearly audible. Both the pings and the echoes are also visible on the oscilloscope screen. Captive dolphins accept a fish only after transmitting sounds in the direction of the fish; so it is clear that the dolphin uses echo location in finding food. The tonal quality of the dolphin sounds varies with the rate of pinging. Often these sounds are emitted slowly enough to be heard as separate pings. But if they are increased to about two dozen or more per second, a tonelike effect results; and when the pings are stepped up to over 100 per second, sounds resembling a groaning, mewing, or moaning, or any of those previously described, may be heard.

By bouncing sound pulsations off underwater objects, the dolphin determines the shape of the target or obstruction as well as the direction and distance to it. Fish can be distinguished from a rock, for example. The "rusty hinge" sound is the audible part of the sonar sound—or rather series of sounds. Arthur McBride, the first curator of Marineland at St. Augustine, discovered that bottle-nosed dolphins either swim around or, more frequently, leap over a fine-mesh fish net but are caught in a net with a mesh size of ten inches or more. To the bottle-nose a fine-mesh net probably appears to be a solid barrier because of the density of reflected sounds. Some species of porpoises and river dolphins, on the other hand, can detect and avoid any and all nets, regardless of the size of the mesh.

If the water in a dolphin tank is purposely made turbid and a fish then thrown in, the dolphin soon darts across the tank through the murkiness, seizes the fish, and surfaces with the prize in its mouth. If a bottle-nosed dolphin is blindfolded with suction cups placed over its eyes, it can still locate fish swiftly and swim about without apparent difficulty. Using its sonar in the same way, the dolphin navigates across muddy bays and harbors and among the piers of shipping docks with ease.

Although both whales and members of the dolphin family "see" objects in water by sending out sound signals and although both possess a fairly rich vocabulary of other signals, most of the experimentation along this line has been conducted on the dolphin—much of it by Dr. Lilly. When selecting his experimental animal, Lilly decided upon the dolphin for several reasons: for example, the dolphin has a brain approaching man's in size and complexity; it probably has the ability to learn an interspecific language; it is similar to man anatomically and physiologically; it is not too large to deal with; an empathy is usually easily established between subject and investigator; the dolphin can and does make humanoid sounds, often mimicking our speech; and at least one species—the bottle-nosed dolphin—is easily obtained in the warm waters along the Florida and Carolina coasts, near the Virgin Islands, and elsewhere.

Can We Talk with Dolphins?

During the twenty months or so that a young dolphin spends with its mother before being weaned, it probably is taught the dolphin language. Lilly believes that the cultural history of the species, in the form of legends, may be passed on at this time. In other words, since dolphins have no written record, all their accumulated information is passed on vocally from parent to offspring. This method is used by certain primitive tribes of humans today.

In all probability, the intraspecific communication of dolphins is complex and highly descriptive. Lilly believes that these animals may be every bit as intelligent as man, though perhaps in a different way. He remarks that some of the above-water sounds the dolphin makes—but only in the presence of human beings—resemble human laughter, whistles, Bronx cheers, and even word syllables in the high-frequency range. According to Lilly dolphins try to communicate with man, deliberately lowering their vocal frequencies to audible ranges (below 10,000 cycles per second), and vocalizing in air rather than water, just for the benefit of human beings. He is convinced that dolphins are eager to learn from man and have, in fact, already acquired and exhibited uncanny knowledge about human beings, despite the handicaps of an aquatic environment and absence of prehensile limbs.

When attempting to communicate with a nonhuman species, Lilly counsels, it is well to keep two points in mind: The subject must be exposed to long periods of human vocalization; and everything possible should be done to secure and maintain mutual friendship between man and subject—even attempting to see that both enjoy the period of contact.

Dr. Lilly has successfully coaxed dolphins into producing audible sounds in either air or water by causing human vocalizations to be emitted alternately above and below the water's surface. Underwater speakers placed in dolphin holding tanks were connected with microphones in the nearby laboratory. In this way dolphins kept in solitude became accustomed to the sounds of human voices. Underwater microphones, or hydrophones, in the holding tanks conveyed dolphin sounds to speakers located in the laboratory.

For a time the animals emitted only the usual dolphin sounds; but later, whistling games were played between the investigators and the dolphins. The animals also mimicked many human sounds, including letters of the alphabet, words, laughter, and sounds of affection—these having been made often by Mrs. Lilly and directed to the dolphins.

Many mimicking sounds made by dolphins are unintelligible until they have been recorded and played back at a slower speed, when it becomes evident that the big mammals compress our somewhat drawn-out words into tiny spurts of seemingly continuous sound. This, and the fact that dolphins often communicate with each other by means of high-pitched whistles and other sounds, makes it especially difficult to establish free and direct vocal exchange with them. The pitch of the intelligible human voice is limited in range from about 100 to 5,000 cycles per second.

The cetaceans appear to be the only nonprimates possessing a highly efficient and complex "language." Dr. Lilly's investigations of the dolphin may determine whether extensive communication with them is possible and may also discover whether all dolphin "language" is the same or, perhaps, consists of distinctive "dialects" for the different areas the animal inhabits. But even if these efforts are unsuccessful, much of what has been learned from these aquatic mammals can be applied to the study of communication in other species, including any extraterrestrial ones that may be encountered in the future.

8. Primates

Of all the primates, humans are by far the most persistently noisy. We talk at great length about anything and everything —ourselves, others, the weather, and so on. Much of what we say could be classed as trivial. Nonhuman primates vocalize comparatively little, relying to a great degree upon facial expressions and body movements, or simply body position, to get their message across. Virtually all these primates live in groups of varying size, so that communication in some form *is* necessary; but a really elaborate communicative system is not a requirement for their simple way of life. The facial expressions, vocalizations, gestures, and other components of the primate system of communication are not inborn. They must be learned by trial and error if the individual—and hence the group and, ultimately, the species— is to be successful in the struggle for survival.

The rearing of most monkeys and apes is similar to that of most primates. They are scolded when necessary, coddled often, they play and romp much of the day, learn what to eat by watching their mother, learn to produce certain calls in accordance with the situations and circumstances. If the young monkey initiates the improper signal or gives an unsuitable response, he is not long in learning about it; when a juvenile attempts to threaten an adult, he is met with a greater threat, or even attack. If he quickly assumes a submissive attitude, the attack may be averted. Gradually effective communication patterns are built up.

It is sometimes difficult for the observer to decide which facial expressions, body positions, sounds, and so on, constitute signals of communication. The apparent significance of many of them can be determined only when two animals are near each other. Even then, although the action of one animal may elicit a response in another, this may not have been the signaler's intention. For instance, a baboon may take a swipe at a snake; a second baboon who does not see a snake, observes the first animal making "go away" motions to something and reacts by immediately leaving the vicinity.

Although monkeys and apes are usually gregarious, their choice of communicative signals may depend to a large extent on the status of a particular species in its biological community. If a species is subject to predation, for example, sound signals for distance communication may be exploited rather than visual or tactile signals for close-range communication. Another characteristic of primate communication is that signals generally are employed in combination; this has the advantage of making available the full range of communicative systems—auditory, visual, tactile, olfactory, and chemical.

There are 200 species of primates; fewer than 12 of these have been extensively studied in the field. The family *Pongidae* —commonly known as the ape family and including the gibbon, orangutan, chimpanzee, and gorilla—has been diligently observed in the wild; but the Old World monkeys, New World monkeys, and prosimians have until recently been more or less neglected, except in captivity. The Old World monkeys include the rhesus monkeys (or macaques), baboons, mandrills, langurs, sacred hanumans, proboscis monkeys, guenons, and other African monkeys. Within the New World monkey group are found the howler monkeys, squirrel monkeys, spider monkeys, marmosets, and others. The prosimians are the most primitive primates; they include the tree shrews,

This nocturnal angwantibo, a prosimian, needs especially large eyes to detect the small creatures it catches and eats in the dark forest.

lemurs, bush babies, tarsiers, avahis, aye-ayes, and other primitive species. All primates have prehensile, or grasping, hands; those of the apes and man are used most dexterously. Certain primates (for example, the rhesus monkeys) have hands even more advanced than those of the apes, but they do not have the brain power to put them to full use.

Old World monkeys are all quadrupeds; they became separated from other primates during the Oligocene period, about 25 or 30 million years ago. The apes no longer show the primitive type of quadrupedalism. Their arms have become longer, and their bodies shorter and wider, than those of the monkeys. These and other changes have successfully adapted them to life in trees—although some, especially the gorillas, spend much of their time on the ground. It is from the *Pongidae* that the *Hominidae* (of which man is a member) were derived, perhaps three or four million years ago. Imprints inside the skull of the Java Man indicate that he may have had a brain that would permit him some sort of language, however rudimentary. The brain volume was 775 to 900 cubic centimeters—far greater than that of the largest brain recorded for the ape (that of a gorilla, 650 cubic centimeters).

Monkeys and prosimians have been highly successful in the tropics and subtropics of both the New World and the Old World. Forest dwellers, they are present in great numbers and exhibit many behavioral and morphological diversifications. The island of Madagascar boasts more than half the living genera of prosimians. Prosimian ancestors were the progenitors of both New World and Old World monkeys (the former appearing some 30 million years after the latter). The prosimians have inhabited the earth since the first half of the age of mammals, and it was during that period that they showed their greatest diversity. Since then they have disappeared from all temperate and northern regions and from the New World. Prosimians persist in the Old World as small, nocturnal, arboreal forms with prehensile hands and feet. Their faces are not nearly so expressive as those of the monkeys and apes. Their sense of smell appears to be keen, tactile hairs and numerous scent glands are present; but they do not see in color or stereoscopically.

Baboons are large monkeys that sleep in trees but spend a great many of their waking hours on the ground. The fossil record indicates that baboons have lived in Africa for more than a million years. Most field studies so far have been confined to gorillas, chimpanzees, and Old World monkeys.

Chemical Signals

Chemical signals occur most frequently among primates that are subject to predation and have a limited range; the source of these signals is difficult to locate yet they need not penetrate over a long distance. Among the nocturnal, arboreal prosimians, therefore, the sense of smell plays a much more important role than it does among the mainly diurnal, terrestrial monkeys and apes.

The skin of prosimians, especially on the face, feet, and anogenital region, is supplied with sweat and sebaceous glands which probably function in olfactory communication. Tree shrews use their throat and chest glands in marking territories. Some species of lemur have glands located on the forearm and in the armpit. The animal may rub his forearm directly on vegetation to leave a trail, or he may first rub the end of his tail on the forearm glands and then use his tail to leave a scent as he moves about.

Like many mammals, prosimians exhibit a number of behavior patterns associated with urination and defecation that appear to have a communicatory function. Certain lemur species mark with urine, while others smear fecal material about. Males sometimes mark females by rubbing them with their anal regions, and dominant males mark subordinate males in the same manner. The bush baby spreads urine on hands and feet to make scent marks as he moves about his territory; the tarsier also marks his territory with urine.

Specialized skin glands are rare in apes and monkeys, as are associated behavior patterns for marking with such glands or with urine and droppings. Monkeys and apes do not have well-developed olfactory lobes. Animals with less to fear from predators than the prosimians, and with greater mobility, have less need for signalizing their environment with a persistent chemical marker.

Tactile Signals

Sight and sound, used by monkeys and apes for distance communication, are combined with the sense of touch for communication at close range. With improved physical dexterity and well-developed sensory and motor areas in the brain, the primates use the hand rather than the nose to initiate physical contact. In certain circumstances teeth, lips, and tongue are used, as are the tail (if prehensile) and body surface.

Friendliness is demonstrated in a variety of ways. Embracing is one way in which langurs, baboons, gibbons, and chimpanzees show friendly behavior. Baboons often greet one another by mouth-to-mouth contact or by nuzzling the genital region. Touching, pushing, gently biting, and mounting are all practiced as friendly gestures. Chimpanzees that have been separated for some time or have never met usually carry out a rather ritualized greeting sequence upon meeting when on the ground. Usually one ape touches the head or shoulder of the other; often, however, the genital area or thigh may be touched.

Grooming—in which one animal manipulates and mouths the fur of another—is particularly important in species where dominance hierarchy plays a significant role, as (for example) in the rhesus monkeys and baboons. It is an act of true intimacy and closeness such as is found in few other animal groups. All members of a baboon troop take part in grooming one another. This action is carried well beyond the point of necessity so far as cleaning is concerned; it is involved in maintaining peace and cohesion within the group and forms a bond between signaler and recipient. When one animal moves toward another with the intention of grooming, he loudly smacks his lips, and continues to do this during the grooming process.

Rhesus monkeys seldom engage in self-grooming but frequently groom one another. Both males and females groom an approximately equal number of times and for about the same length of time per grooming. When a mother is tending a new infant, other monkeys in the group, especially the females, often groom her—apparently so that they may be near the offspring.

In adult gorillas mutual grooming is far less frequent than in most other species. However, as George Schaller describes in his book *The Mountain Gorilla*, gorilla mothers sometimes impulsively grab infants (not necessarily their own) and start grooming them. Often the infant responds to this gesture by embracing the adult.

Auditory Signals

Monkeys and apes live in close-knit social groupings that are relatively isolated from species similar in size and structure living in the same area. Thus they do not require sound communication with a high degree of specificity and are free to exploit systems of simpler and noisier sounds, such as "drumming," or chest beating, that carry over a long distance.

The chimpanzee, for example, strikes rapid blows on the buttress roots of large trees. Howls, hoots, squeals, or other vocalizations accompany this drumming, although the howls are often produced without drumming. The drumming sounds can often be heard for a mile or more, usually traveling a greater distance than the sounds emitted by the animals themselves. Drumming may serve to inform groups of chimpanzees that there are others of their kind in the area; but there is some evidence that the action also is concerned with the calling of several different groups of chimpanzees to a site where food is particularly abundant. Eight times during their nine months' stay in the Budonga Forest of the Congo, Vernon and Frances Reynolds noted that chimpanzees held drumming and "singing" festivals, each of several hours' duration.

Gorillas make a somewhat similar sound by slapping their

chests with their hands. Just prior to beginning this action, they inflate air sacs in the chests. Although air sacs of various types are common in primates, only gorillas are known to use them to produce sound. Chest slapping climaxes a series of at least nine separate acts, including sitting up, head tipping, giving forth a chain of hooting sounds which eventually become a growl, rising to a bipedal position, and tearing up vegetation and tossing it into the air. The animal often places a leaf between his lips at some point in the routine. During the actual chest slapping, the hands, somewhat cupped, slap the lower chest region as many as twenty times. The rate is some ten slaps each second. Just as the gorilla finishes the slapping procedure, he sometimes skips sideways, like a

American Museum of Natural History

Gorillas are well known for their act of chest slapping. This display is the climax of a series of separate motions that the gorilla performs to warn of some impending danger.

football player in a shift, then runs forward. There is real danger to bystanders during this shifting and running, because at this time the gorilla may swing at anything, plant or animal, that he encounters.

The chest-beating display is almost certainly instinctive. Zoo animals have been observed to slap their chests when only a few months old, even though they had never seen another gorilla do so. Eventually these juveniles also stick a leaf between their lips, hoot, and throw vegetation.

The survival value of the chest-slapping routine, performed in its entirety only by the leader of a gorilla group (although females do parts of it), is obvious. It tells fellow members of the group that an enemy is near, and it serves as a very effective warning and intimidation to an outsider. The sight of man, the approach of a strange gorilla or group, a brief glimpse of an unidentified animal or animals, and other circumstances may elicit a chest-slapping sequence. Sometimes one or two other gorillas may join the first signaler in a contagion reaction. Schaller describes the chest beating of the gorilla as making a *pok-pok-pok-pok* sound that is sometimes difficult to locate or judge in terms of distance.

Basically the vocalizing systems of humans and lower primates are quite similar. All have a larynx and vocal membrane, and during phonation a column of air is sent forcibly through the voice box by the respiratory muscles, acting in bellowslike fashion.

Although some of the sounds made during the vocalizations of nonhuman primates are fairly pure in tone, or "clear," this seems to be the exception rather than the rule. Primate calls are for the most part coarse in character—even "noisy." Some primates produce birdlike sounds; but their vocalizations in the main range between 4,000 and 5,000 cycles per second.

Primates as a group have a vocal repertoire of approximately ten to twenty sound signals. Definite, repetitive vocal signals may be rare in or even absent from the communicative sequences of the apes and higher monkeys. Loudness or intensity, rate of repetition, pitch, and other qualities often vary from one spectrogram to the next, even when a series (as many as fifteen) of these recordings are made under very similar circumstances.

Internal need seems to dictate the type of vocalizing done by human infants and by young and adult nonhuman primates. Cries of pain, hunger, fear, and distress are common; and the adult nonhuman primate adds to these signals mating calls, expressions of anger and threat, and so on.

Clicking and chittering noises are made by juveniles of some species. This type of sound is among the easiest to locate in space, thus ensuring that the signaler will not be missed or ignored. The usually quiet and secretive bush baby, for example, occasionally makes clicking and crackling noises to attract attention.

Squealing also might be regarded as a specialty of the infant and juvenile. The first sounds heard each day from a troop of langurs are the squeals of the very young at dawn. Soon the adults begin grunting, and the daily activity is under way. At bedding-down time in the evening, grunting and squealing are heard for an hour or so, until finally all becomes quiet. If a mother leaves a young chimpanzee for even a short time, squealing is prompt and continuous, accompanied by physical displays of obvious agitation and anxiety.

Squeals are also sprinkled throughout such traveling and feeding calls as grunts and panting hoots. The teeth and gums are exposed during squealing, but the jaws remain closed or nearly so.

Environmental information concerning food, predators, and other physical objects is communicated less frequently in primates than in other animals. Changes in the mood of members of the group, coordination of its social activities— particularly those associated with the dominance hierarchy— and similar motivational information, on the other hand, are represented to a marked degree.

A variety of sounds are used, singly or in combination, as alarm signals. Barks, frequently shrill, are given by langurs and howler monkeys at the approach of a predator. Baboons emit a loud two-phase sound that carries over a distance of more than half a mile. When startled, a baboon gives a single, extrashrill bark.

While observing chimpanzees in Nigeria's Gombe Stream Reserve, Jane Goodall noted that both high- and low-pitched barks are given by groups of these animals that are excited for one reason or another. A high-pitched bark is often used by individuals seeking to intimidate humans or baboons. Threats also sometimes take the form of panting barks of rather low pitch, accompanied by a show of teeth and elevation of the arm in the direction of the animal under threat. When a chimpanzee spies a human or a large animal such as a buffalo, he often opens his mouth slightly and, without baring his teeth, emits a chain of sharp barks. An audible grating noise is made in conjunction with these barks.

Many of the communicatory signals made by baboons have to do with protection of the group. An effectively startling alarm signal is one made up of a single extraloud bark, produced by the first baboon to spot an animal such as a hyena or even an antelope. When this call is given, all baboons within earshot make a mad dash to leave the area, often leaping into trees. When a predator such as a lion is seen, the startle call is entirely different; in this instance the bark of the baboon is of a distinctly different quality, travels farther, and is repeated over and over again.

When restless the Budonga chimpanzee may decide to move about or come down from a tree. This action is often accompanied by high-pitched barks that often blend into a scream. Upon becoming mildly excited, as when they hear the calls of another group, chimpanzees often produce a series of so-called panting barks. These are low-pitched barking sounds, each followed by a noisy sucking in of the breath.

Schaller observed, photographed, and recorded the vocalizing of eleven separate and distinct groups of gorillas in the Virunga Volcano region of the Congo. He found that when a gorilla leader wishes to warn his group of impending danger, for example, he may bark nervously for a time, then bring the barks to high pitch for emphasis. If he wishes to warn an enemy, such as the leader of a strange gorilla group, he may roar, hoot, or emit shattering screams, accompanied by flat-handed slaps on his chest and on the ground.

Soft grunts are used by primates as they travel along together, apparently as a means of maintaining contact among members of the group. C. R. Carpenter has been systematically observing howler monkeys on the island of Barro Colorado in Panama for over thirty years. He discovered that when an adult male howler wants other members of his group to pay attention to him, he emits a chain of grunts in rapid succession, as follows: *who-who-who-who-who*. The adult also keeps young howlers from becoming too boisterous in play by making a low grunting sound.

The most common sound in the baboon repertoire is the grunt. It carries several different and distinct meanings, which depend upon the circumstances under which the grunt is given, whether it is high pitched or low pitched, whether it is given in phases or as a continuous sound, and other variables. If uttered by an adult male as a two-phased *uh-huh*, the grunt is sometimes a precursor to a loud warning or fighting roar. The roar—actually a very intense grunting—consists of two phases. The vast majority of baboon roars are made by combating adult males.

Apparently a dominant male is responsible for the grunting in chorus that takes place when a group of baboons are bedding down for the night. He begins the low, repetitious vocalizing, and one by one the others chime in. This same pattern of grunting is also heard when baboons are feeding quietly in fairly close aggregation. At night it probably serves as a lullaby for the young.

When a male chimpanzee decides to move, he may produce a strong, low-pitched, grunting *hoo*, looking at the other members of the group as he does so. In response they look at him briefly, then move along with him. What apparently is the same call, but at a greater volume, is sometimes given when an individual feels some anxiety from being watched by a human observer.

When two chimpanzees approach and greet each other, or eat from the same food source, or engage in mutual grooming,

Teeth bared and fur erect, this hamadryad baboon is communicating an unmistakable threat to another creature. Teeth-
baring alone can also mean other things, including fear. These
baboons were common in ancient Egypt, where they were
revered as oracles when alive and often mummified after
death.

they often exchange a chain of panting grunts, low in pitch; these are described by Jane Goodall as sounding like *ah-e-ach* or *ugh-e-ugh*.

When gorillas are resting or feeding quietly, vocalizing is restricted to four rather low-volume sounds, apparently indicating that the animals are content. These are perhaps best described as a purring sound, a grumble, a grunt, and a humming sound. The purr and the grunt are particularly soft. A couple of short, crisp grunting sounds from a leader tells the rest of the group that danger may be near; the females and young gorillas, heeding the warning, promptly move close to the leader.

There are several vocalizations characteristic of a dispersed or moving group of gorillas.* For example, there are short, low-pitched grunts, given in a chain of from two to eight short, clear, but soft *u-u-u*, *ü-ü-ü*, or *wo-wo-wo* sounds. Next a *bo-bo-bo* call may be given. This call is highly variable, and is emitted in a chain of *bo-bo-bo*'s given over and over in rapid succession. At other times calls sounding like *ho-ho-ho-hi-ho-ho*, *o-o-o-o o-o-o-o*, or *bu-bu-bu* may be used.

When a gorilla leader wants to bring his foraging group together, his call is very distinctive. Schaller describes it as *u-u-u*; it is rather low in pitch and actually consists of a series of calls rather than one continuous sound. If the group has wandered particularly far, the call sometimes changes to one that alternately rises and falls in pitch. In any event, when the leader gives one of these calls he is announcing his location, so that his charges will not stray.

Whoops and howls sometimes function as a spacing mechanism, to keep groups of primates apart. When a group of langurs is preparing to travel a long way or to make a rapid

---

* Vocalizations used by the express permission of Dr. George B. Schaller in *The Mountain Gorilla* and *The Year of the Gorilla* (Chicago, The University of Chicago Press, 1964). Schaller gives his gorilla vocalizations German pronunciations; for example, he refers to the German word *kümmel* as an aid to pronouncing a sound he describes as *ü-ü-ü*, and to *könig* in order to show how his *ö* should be pronounced. In his *u-u-u*, the *u* sounds like the *oo* in "soot"; the *o* in *wo-wo* is like that of "rote"; in *hi*, the *i* is like *ee*; the *u* in *hu-hu* is like that of "flute"; and the *a* in *ha* is like *ah*.

move, the adult males produce low-pitched whoops, whose resonating quality makes them carry over a considerable distance. Separate howler groups, even when 200 or 300 yards apart, may become so excited that they set up a din lasting three or four hours. The loud burping noises produced by adult male orangutans by inflating the air sacs under their chins may be territorial defense signals as well as significant in the dominance hierarchy and in mating.

The many and varied sounds made by gorillas are for the most part low pitched, ranging from about 100 to 2,000 cycles per second. The explosive roar so often described by observers is given only by male gorillas—more specifically, by silver-backed leaders and large blackbacked males. The intensity of the roar usually varies with the emotional state of the animal: the angrier or more excited he becomes, the more violent and explosive the roar. A typical low-intensity roar has two or three tones but is slurred into one continuous sound. Schaller represents such a roar in the following manner:

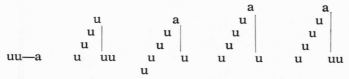

Roars serve both as warnings to other members of the group and as threats to intruders, especially human ones. Few Africans will remain near a group of gorillas after a loud roar. Other gorillas gather closely around a male that gives a warning roar.

Vocalizations of fear are of two chief types: high-pitched screams and screaming roars. Apparently containing elements of both fear and anger, the screaming roar takes on more of the quality of a scream as fear increases. In the case of the high-pitched scream, especially when given by females and young gorillas, there is not much doubt as to meaning: it is a signal of fear and always produces response by other members of the group.

Schaller found that a gorilla male could warn him to stay

away without exciting the other members of the group; there is a difference between warnings meant for outsiders and those meant for fellow gorillas. One gorilla roared at him time and again, while the other members of the group took no apparent notice. But this was not always the case; when the roaring gorilla happened to be a leader, the gorillas were often just as startled as Schaller.

Baboon babies need this kind of normal interplay with their mother to grow up into emotionally mature animals. Without such activity they might never be able to function as adults, especially with sex partners, even after achieving full physical development.

Visual Signals

Many monkeys and apes rely upon gestures and facial expressions for much of their communication. Among these groups vocalizations are used chiefly as alerting sounds. When a group member hears them, he watches for facial expressions and gestures or for some other visual signal. When the *proboscis* monkey of Borneo displays his enormous nose, or the mandrill of West Africa shows off his vivid facial coloration, their fellow monkeys sense that the exhibitor is to be respected. Both the nose of the proboscis monkey and the colors of the mandrill serve as warning devices to other members of the troop and to outside intruders; they are also used in courtship displays.

There are many visual signals associated with threat or attack. These include piloerection of the mantle hairs, bipedal stance, and a hunching forward of the shoulders; or the hands may rotate or thump the ground. Wild, aimless throwing of stones occurs, and sometimes vegetation is grabbed and shaken violently.

When Phyllis Jay made field studies of langurs, she avoided looking directly into their faces—because as is the case with other primates (and other animals), a direct stare is considered a threat. In order to better establish rapport with a group of langurs, she made sure that she not only avoided staring but moved away when threatened by the monkeys.

Dominant male baboons spend much of their time threatening others in the troop. Sometimes a threat will be limited to a long, hard stare. When a baboon uses a stare as a threat, the light-colored eyelids often blink rapidly, the head moves up and down, and the eyebrows are raised in high arches. The ears are pulled tightly against the head. At other times the stare may be accompanied by a one-handed thump or slap in the direction of the animal being threatened; or the aggressor may simply rise to a bipedal position and stare. The fur of his mane stands out, causing him to look much larger than he actually is. If the threatened animal does not immediately respond to these tactics, the dominant baboon will launch a swift physical attack, barking loudly as he does so. If the victim is unable to evade the attacker, he finds himself clamped in the jaws of the dominant male, usually by the nape of the neck. The baboon does not often do physical harm to his victim, but he may go so far as to rub the subordinate animal on the ground or beat him with his hands.

Almost without fail a gorilla leader can quiet a pair of females with a few well-chosen grunts, but in the event that no heed is taken, the leader uses his never-failing peace-maker—the stone-cold stare. A huge male gorilla, staring straight into the face of a misbehaving female or juvenile, is saying in effect: "Now, look here! You stop this nonsense immediately, or I'll really have to get tough!" In gorilla language a stare can also be a challenge. When two strange gorillas come unexpectedly face to face, they roar, back away, slap their chests and the ground, and rush at each other at express-train speed. Just short of collision they stop, with faces all but touching, each staring straight into the dark eyes of the other. Eventually one gorilla will back away, but the whole performance may be repeated until one animal leaves, taking his group to other territory.

Some signals, such as tongue movement, lip smacking, ear flattening, grimacing, and yawning, have both friendly and unfriendly connotations. Moving the tongue in and out of the mouth is a submissive gesture used on occasion by the male langur, and may be accompanied by soft grunts. The female seems to do more tongue moving than the male; she may either grunt or squeal when she makes this signal. Lip smack-ing is used as a friendly greeting by adult baboons. Ear flatten-ing, unaccompanied by yawning and raised eyebrows, is also a sign of friendliness, as are the acts of presenting and of assuming a bipedal stance. When a baboon is apprehensive, afraid, or seeking to escape danger, there are several telltale signs he may make that indicate his emotional state. Rather surprisingly, yawning is one of these signs. In this case the yawn is not accompanied by the other signs that express threat.

The facial expressions of the chimpanzee are numerous. They often reflect the personality of the individual animal as well as his emotional state at any particular time. If the jaws are clamped shut but the teeth and gums are exposed, the animal is warning or threatening another. Even subordinate chimps sometimes use this display in the hope of warding off a more dominant animal. When a male chimpanzee makes a real or tentative charge toward another animal or a human, his best scowl goes with him; it serves to intimidate his intended victim. As the older infants and younger juveniles go about their daily romps, they can often be seen to smile or stick out their tongues, letting each other know that their activities are all in fun. When adults wish to show affection to a juvenile or infant, they may stick out their lips in a sort of pout, and even kiss the young chimp on the buttock. A yawn is sometimes indicative of bewilderment or uncertainty —a displacement reaction. A chimpanzee may make this display over and over again as he sits in a tree, undecided as to whether or not he should move out of sight of a human watching him from the ground.

The eyes of a gorilla are very expressive. Schaller claims that by looking into a gorilla's eyes, he can tell whether the animal is uneasy, annoyed, or merely curious. Gorillas can tell what a movement or gesture means much more quickly and correctly than a man. Some males, when watched by a man, yawn repeatedly. It is not known whether this action is of any communicative value, but it seems to indicate uneasiness in the gorilla. Instead of yawning, other animals may shake their heads from side to side when stared at; occasionally as they do this, they may allow the lower jaw to hang open, producing a rattling sound. Like baboons and chimpanzees, the gorilla sometimes bares his teeth in anger or warning. The act is often accompanied by an appropriate scream.

In certain primates as in many mammals, the tail has special communicative significance. For example, the male lemur's long tail moves rhythmically before he touches it to the marking gland on his forearm, and during mating. The estrous female langur lowers her tail and allows it to touch the ground. Male primates customarily raise their tails as a sign of subordination.

In rhesus monkeys visual cues are used almost exclusively by subordinate animals, who promptly leave an area that dominant monkeys are in the process of occupying (provided they see the upper-class animals in time to avoid a fight). Subordinate rhesus monkeys show their status in sev-

Woodland chimpanzees in Tanzania have been observed sticking twigs into termite nests to catch and eat the termites that bite into the intruding object. Often they will work one nest for hours, shaping or replacing their twigs as they become bent or broken. Jane Goodall, one scientist who observed this behavior, believes that it is not instinctive but rather is learned from other chimpanzees and handed down through the ape community.

eral ways. If a dominant animal draws near, one of lower
rank may flatten his ears and, with jaws closed, smack his
lips; or he may quickly raise his tail and present.

The subordinate baboon combines wide-eyed stares, grins,
and sidelong looks to indicate that he is afraid, or at least
in a state of uncertainty. Sometimes the shoulders are
shrugged, the mouth is wiped with the hand, or the body is
scratched aimlessly. An erect tail is an indication of subordination. If a baboon is very much afraid, he may prostrate
himself and grow rigid. When an infant feels insecure or apprehensive after being separated from his mother, his head
and upper extremities may tremble visibly.

One of the outstanding evidences of social status in the
baboon world is the act of presenting. A subordinate animal
often takes up a position in front of a more dominant baboon
and raises his tail, waiting nervously. More often than not,
the dominant animal ignores this invitation to mount.

In sharp contrast to the baboons and many other primates,
the chimpanzees have no strong dominance hierarchy. If there
is one desire that appears to be uppermost in the chimp's
mind, it is to preserve the peace with animals that are even
temporarily of higher rank than he. One expression used by a
subordinate chimpanzee—known as the appeasement grin—
is made by pulling down the lower lip until the teeth and
gums are exposed. Sometimes the grinning ape adds the gesture of touching the scrotum or lips of the dominant animal.

As an act of submission, a gorilla cowers in the presence of
a dominant animal. The cowering gorilla crouches low, sometimes placing his hands over the back of his head. The dominant gorilla always honors this plea for mercy. Even infants
cease to wrestle when one, usually the smaller of the two,
cowers.

Among the langurs dominance is demonstrated more subtly.
Every group of langurs has a dominant male who serves as
leader. He is never a tyrant or dictator; in fact, when observed
in a peacefully moving or feeding group of these monkeys, he
seems to be just "one of the boys." After a time, however,
the "number one" and "number two" males of the hierarchy

can be picked out without a great amount of difficulty. The very act of quietly pausing or hesitating is a signal of dominancy on the part of the one who hesitates. For example, if a langur sits resting or feeding and another passing animal stops briefly *by his side*, the indication is that the sitting animal is the subordinate one. He will turn away or leave his position. On the other hand, if one langur pauses *in front* of another, the one who pauses is the subordinate monkey. Sometimes the mere act of drawing near or reaching out and lightly touching a subordinate animal, when performed by a dominant animal, causes the lower-ranking monkey to move away. A first-ranking or second-ranking male langur often brings about a submissive reaction in a lower-status monkey simply by making a slight change in posture or by focusing his eyes in a certain manner.

The prestige and respect accorded the more dominant male bonnet macaques of southern India are carried over into old age. Even when a male belonging to the central core of the group has become very old and has lost his canine teeth, he has but to walk into the midst of a group of threatening males, and all quarreling comes to an abrupt halt. Subadult males—young, much stronger, and with sharp, white canines —never threaten him.

The baboon's place in a dominance hierarchy, or even his degree of nervous tension, is often revealed by the manner in which he stands or walks. Quietly but confidently a dominant male baboon moves through an area, tail raised, with a stiff-legged gait. He is constantly on the alert; any change in the characteristic mannerisms of the leader warns other animals in the group that they should adjust accordingly. For example, if the dominant male sits down and relaxes by arching his back and lowering his head, the other baboons know that they may safely follow suit.

Middle-aged silverbacked male gorillas (so named for the large patch of silver-gray hair covering part of the back, shoulders, and neck) dominate all other members of a gorilla group. Only one of these males acts as leader at any one time. A gorilla leader always signals to the others in his group when he wishes to move on, also indicating what direction he wishes to take. Sometimes he utters a half-dozen or so emphatic grunts as he stands spraddle legged, facing the direction in which he intends to move. More typically, however, he simply rises from the feeding or resting area and immediately moves off toward another location. As he does so, he walks with a peculiar stiff-legged gait, moving at what is relatively a much faster rate of speed than usual.

Interspecific Communication

As a defense against predation, a number of primates of entirely different species have evolved an effective system of mutual assistance. Langurs, for example, pay close attention to alarm calls or even sudden movements of such animals as peacocks and deer. The bark of a spotted deer (whose eyesight is extremely sharp) often warns langurs of approaching intruders, including man, much sooner than the monkey sees them.

The ungulates and the baboons each know the alarm calls of the other; and the fine senses of smell and hearing in the ungulates complement the sharp visual ability of the baboons. Surprise attack by a mutual enemy is unlikely. Irven De Vore and K. R. L. Hall tell of an instance in which three cheetahs, which are regular predators of the impala, stalked a mixed group of baboons and impala. A large male baboon, eyes fixed, moved toward the cheetahs, and they promptly left the scene. During this quiet contest of stalk and bluff, the impala appeared to be alert; but they also showed their confidence in the baboons by not attempting to flee.

In Nairobi Park, Kenya, a parasitologist shot two baboons from a car. The animals were members of a large group being studied by an animal behaviorist, who always approached the baboons in a car. Only a few of the animals actually saw the killing; nevertheless, even eight months later the group remained unapproachable by automobile. Perhaps those animals that had witnessed the shooting warned the others whenever a car was seen or heard; or perhaps the potential

American Museum of Natural History
Young chimpanzees have a great need for the physical presence of their parents. When its mother leaves it, the young
chimp protests with loud squeals and displays of agitation.

danger of automobiles was instilled into every member of the group by the danger signals transmitted by those animals that actually saw the shooting.

Chimpanzees may be alerted by the alarm calls of baboons, other species of monkey, bushbucks, and several bird species. On hearing such a call, the chimp looks around to discover the nature of the danger, then may become uneasy and move away.

Apes, monkeys, and prosimians have progressed to their present state of physical and social development, as have other animals, by the evolutionary process of natural selection. The role played in this process by communication, though obviously a vital one, is at present poorly defined. With the rapid development of instrumentation, a whole new spectrum of possibilities is opened to the investigator, offering hope for the solution of puzzles man has often felt were unsolvable. Herein lies a challenge; a more intriguing one would be difficult to find. Why communication was first favored by natural selection as an aid to species survival we do not at this moment know. The solutions to this problem and to many others are, hopefully, on their way. Increased knowledge of the nonhuman primates may help man to better understand himself in the future.

9. Methods and Tools for Study

The obstacles encountered in the study of animal communication are many and great. The environment of free-living animals ranges from dense tropical rain forests on the one hand to arid wastes on the other; from the lofty altitudes of our highest mountains to the depths of the sea; and from the bitter cold of the polar regions to the heat of the equator. Much of the information found in reports concerning animal communication is speculative in nature. A certain amount of work has been done concerning communicative signals; but studies of the responses to these signals have on the whole been neglected.

Considering our present level of understanding regarding social communication in animals, a pragmatic approach might be a feasible one. This method of attacking the problem would require that both observational and experimental work be carried out in the field and that a thorough knowledge of characteristic responses to given signals be obtained. At the present time the assessment and evaluation of communicatory patterns are of a syntactical or typological nature, and the apparent significance of signals is arrived at by extrapolation. By inductive (and often subjective) reasoning the investigator must reach a large number of decisions as to the possible significance of his observations.

The two most generally employed investigative methods—

observation and experiment—may be conducted in the field or in the laboratory. Laboratory investigation offers the opportunity to concentrate on specialized problems, such as sensory discrimination and learning. In the field the investigator is concerned with a broader spectrum of problems relating to the animal in its environment. The particular methods used vary with the investigator, the funds and equipment available, the animal under consideration, the environment of the animal, and such other factors as whether the animal happens to be in captivity or free to roam his natural habitat while the study is being carried out.

Observation

The oldest and still one of the most useful ways in which to study animals is by observing them in action. Detailed notes, made at the time an animal sound or movement is being recorded or photographed, contribute much toward arriving at a working hypothesis. Ideally the subject is observed in his natural habitat, but this is not always practical—especially in the case of far-ranging mammals or of microscopic forms of life. Much valuable information has been obtained, however, by observing animals in captivity.

Although an animal cannot be assumed to behave in captivity exactly as it would in its native habitat, there are certain advantages to laboratory observation that are not to be had in the field. Here the animal's physical behavior can be observed at first hand; and although it might be borne in mind that actions in an artificial environment do not necessarily approximate those in the natural environment, it has recently been found that in many cases there is a high degree of similarity between the two. Fishes and aquatic invertebrates are often placed in controlled environments, where they are photographed and their sounds recorded. As with aquatic mammals, the most thorough studies can take place only in a relatively restricted environment rather than in the natural habitat.

Incredible patience is necessary when studying birds in

the field; they can be frightened away by the slightest movement or sight of man, or by the warning cries of other birds (notably the jay and crow). Anyone wishing to observe birds would do well to consider building a blind and resigning himself to sitting in it, often unrewarded, hour after hour. Amphibians are highly secretive in their natural habitats and extremely lethargic in captivity. They can be studied better at night than during the day, since they are nocturnal in their feeding and mating habits. This also holds true for many reptiles and land mammals.

The land mammals, in fact, are among the most difficult animals to study. When they are in their natural environment, they tend to move about a lot; when held in captivity, they tend to arrest or cease completely many of the activities they carried out in the wild. Blinds—rough enclosures of brush and sticks, with peepholes or cracks for the observer—and tree platforms are useful in observing and photographing land mammals. In both cases the observer must begin by selecting a likely spot, first scrutinizing droppings, footprints, and other signs, rather than setting up a post in a haphazard manner and then hoping some animal will come along. Often a biologist's scent will give him away; to overcome this he uses a stronger scent to mask his own. The common method is to carry a small bottle of skunk mercaptan and occasionally sprinkle a very few drops about. This is an extremely effective procedure if the person using the mercaptan can successfully tolerate its powerful odor.

Studies may involve an analysis of the signals themselves, the behavior of the signaler, or that of the recipient. Ultrasonic sounds, for example, are detected and analyzed by electronic apparatus (discussed later in this chapter). Motion-picture cameras have proved useful in the recording of visual and tactile signals, while chemists have been able to isolate color pattern pigments as well as musk and similar attractants produced as chemical signals. The various components of signals, the variations in their production, and the circumstances in which they are used all require a great deal of additional study.

This research worker is blowing on a whistle with which he can reproduce the call of the hummingbird. With his highly sensitive earphones and microphone he can hear these little birds as they approach, then switch on his tape recorder to record the sounds they make. The broad disk attached to the microphone is constructed in a parabolic curve that focuses all sound waves striking the disk on the "mike" at the center. This device is basic equipment for all students of bird sounds.

There is still much we do not know about the relation to their functions of the specialized structures that send out signals; the same is true of environmental influences. Both internal, or physiological, and external environments affect the signal an animal produces or the response it makes to a given signal. In the spring, for instance, increased production of the hormone testosterone causes some birds to sing in a particular manner that is used at no other time of year. External temperatures affect the internal temperatures of animals that do not have constant body temperature. For example, certain grasshoppers and crickets have minimum and maximum temperatures for singing: they sing more and more slowly as the temperature drops, until finally they become absolutely quiet.

Electrophysiological methods have long been used in studying the auditory and visual organs of mammals, birds, and insects. The electroencephalogram, for instance, varies from the normal when an animal is stimulated in various ways. Electrodes placed on sensory nerves indicate the level of response of an organ such as an eye or ear by recording a change in electrical potential when a given stimulus is applied at an experimentally determined strength or in a particular manner or amount.

Responses such as withdrawal or approach may be noted, as well as the orientation of the signal recipient to the signaler and the correlation between signal variation and response variation.

Experiment

The experimental channels already open to the naturalist who would know more about animal communication are many and varied; in fact it might be said that the methods available are limited only by the ingenuity of the experimenter. Often the results of laboratory studies can be correlated with those made in the field so that a greater amount of information is obtained than would be possible from either if considered alone.

Birds and other animals often respond to crudely constructed likenesses of their kind. By adding to and substracting from the element (coloration, for instance) in these dummy animals that evokes a given response, that response can be analyzed in detail. How some of the insects produce certain sounds is at the present time a mystery; perhaps these sounds could be produced by artificial means, in an effort to better understand their origins. Tape recordings of animal sounds can be edited and played back to members of the same species in an effort to ascertain the response elicited by certain parts of a sound or series of sounds. Computers can be programed for spectographic characteristics of ani-

Robert C. Hermes
Great patience is required of anyone who wishes to observe or photograph wild animals. Here naturalist Robert C. Hermes takes pictures of wild birds with a telescopic camera.

mal sounds to reveal similarity in responses on the part of sender and receiver, as in the case of investigations on the dolphin. And the development of sophisticated physiochemical techniques for dealing with trace components can accelerate the already spectacular advances made in pheromonic research. A number of insect sex attractants, for example, have been chemically identified and synthesized in pure form, while behavioral experiments have indicated the presence of many others in a wide range of insects.

Signals as well as the structures that produce them can be modified. Surgery can be used as an aid to determine the function of a particular body organ or structure. Isolation of animal subjects may also expand our knowledge, by modifying development of the communicatory signals. Among primates, for example, certain signals of communication require training by parents and other older group members, or at least the presence of these animals, so that the young may observe and imitate them. By isolating newborn monkeys from mature monkeys, it is noted that certain communicatory patterns necessary to the animals' social development never appear—unless the isolated animals are given the opportunity to associate with the older monkeys or even with their chronological equals.

Equipment

The nature of the information that is to be observed and recorded varies with the training of the investigator and with the type of problem under consideration. In turn, it dictates the type of equipment that is needed for a particular investigation.

One of the most important tools employed by any animal investigator is his notebook. Clear, concise notes made *at the time of the observation or experiment* and listing all pertinent data—including remarks about the weather, season, environment, presence or absence of other animals, even the time of day or night—provide invaluable reinforcing evidence when used in conjunction with photographs or recordings. Many a biologist has found to his regret that his memory is far from infallible, even a short time after conducting an experiment in the field or in the laboratory.

Other basic field equipment should include a flashlight, a compass, and high-powered binoculars—7 × 35, 7 × 50, or 8 × 30, as a general rule. Since many mammals are nocturnal, field investigations of these animals require specialized equipment, such as the "sniperscope" and infrared film. The type of camera used varies greatly according to the animal species to be studied and its habitat. A 35-mm. camera with 50-mm. or 135-mm. lens is generally satisfactory. A motion picture camera can be used to good advantage because it permits frame-by-frame analysis as well as keeping a complete record; however, film is expensive, and animals are at times quite unpredictable. You can never be sure that the action you want is the action that ends up on film.

Many amphibians may be captured simply by shining a bright light into their eyes and picking them up by net, or even in the hand. Snakes are best captured by using snake tongs or clamps designed for the purpose. In the snake-infested swamplands of the Deep South, many outdoorsmen wear high boots or metal leggings made of stovepipe as an aid in avoiding snakebite. Snakes are lethargic when cold and extremely active when warm. This holds true of most other amphibians and reptiles and must be taken into consideration when planning a study project involving these animals.

Thanks to the giant strides made in the development of technology and equipment in recent years, particularly in the field of electronics, it is now possible to explore the ocean in a manner that was completely unknown only a few years ago. One of the most valuable ways in which ocean depths can be investigated is by eavesdropping with the aid of newly devised sound equipment. For instance, hydrophones can be connected to high-gain amplifying equipment which in turn is coupled with recording apparatus. A modern addition to recording equipment is the sound spectrograph; another instrument utilized might be a cathode-ray oscilloscope. The spectrograph makes a permanent record, while the oscilloscope usually acts as a monitoring device. The sounds of a school of dolphins make visible "blips" on the small television-type oscilloscope screen. Although these blips appear temporarily, they can be photographed by a motion-picture camera just as they occur.

The sound spectrograph is manufactured by the Kay Electric Company, of New Jersey; credit for its invention, however, should go to the Bell Telephone Laboratories. In making a spectrogram (the record produced by the spectrograph), animal sounds are first recorded by means of a conventional magnetic-tape recorder. These are then played back, meanwhile being fed into the sound spectrograph by means of a connecting cable. As the spectrograph receives electronic impulses from the tape, it converts them into motion, so that a stylus makes an ink tracing on chart paper attached to a revolving drum. This special paper is ruled off in graphic increments, indicating the sound frequency (in kilocycles) along the ordinate and the duration of the sound along the abscissa. The approximate amplitude is indicated by the relative heaviness of the line traced by the stylus. A more precise picture of amplitude can be obtained by adjusting the apparatus so that it records amplitude rather than time along the abscissa; however, no time interval is indicated when the machine is used in this manner.

The spectrograph reveals a multitude of facts about animal sounds. For instance, a series of bird chirpings may sound very similar to the human ear, but the spectrograph may show that the singer is performing half a dozen or more separate and distinctly different songs in rapid succession, each with its own meaning or implication for other members of the same (or even other) species within hearing distance. W. H. Thorpe, the English ornithologist, found that by studying sound spectrograms and with a good deal of practice he was able to determine approximately how the graphically recorded notes of a birdsong would sound to humans. He pointed out that recordings of harsh and unmelodious sounds produce an unsystematic, dispersed series of tracings on the spectrogram; on the other hand, those tracings showing systematic patterns of concentrated energy are made by sounds of much higher tonal quality.

The spectrograph does not reveal the meaning of any of

the sounds made by animals—at least not yet. It is, however, a valuable research tool when used in conjunction with other devices in a program involving the analysis of sounds.

Highly useful also is the variable-speed tape recorder. It has been in common use in both the field and the laboratory for a number of years and has proven its worth many times over. With the tape recorder, sounds are quickly and easily preserved for detailed study and analysis. When used with various accessories—hydrophones for the recording of underwater sounds, for example, or supersensitive microphones and parabolic reflectors for the recording of extremely high-frequency sounds, such as those made by certain birds and insects—the tape recorder is the most versatile single instrument the biologist can have at his disposal. Bird calls have been recorded with particular success using the tape recorder and parabolic reflector. Microphones, too, can be fired by slingshot over limbs containing bird nests or simply suspended in trees where birds are known to nest. Many satisfactory recordings have been made in aviaries; and birds have been induced to call through injections with hormones. George Schaller and Jane Goodall, in their pioneering researches on gorillas and chimpanzees, respectively, supplemented their notes, photographs, and observations with tape recordings to compile data on these primates as they went about their daily business of feeding, resting, nest building, grooming, and play.

One of the latest devices for trying to unlock the secret door to comprehension of dolphin language is the Sceptron pattern recognizer, developed by the Sperry Gyroscope Company. This miniature computer "memorizes" sounds of dolphins or other animals, records communicatory patterns among dolphins and between man and dolphin, and catalogs dolphin noises in order to translate them into meaningful communication with human beings.

The scientific world eagerly awaits the further development and subsequent decrease in price of the magnetic-tape television camera. With this electronic device it becomes possible not only to record the sounds being made by an animal, but to secure a visual record of its actions as well. Portions of the projected tape may be photographed as desired, and the tape itself may be used over and over again. The camera does not require a projector since an ordinary television set may be used.

Today we can detect the often ultrasonic sounds of dolphins and record them, then play them back at slower speeds for analysis. This, however, is a time-consuming procedure. What is needed is an instrument that will instantly lower the pitch of the dolphin's vocalizations and perhaps simultaneously raise the pitch of our own, so that we may more conveniently relate speech to action, discover the significance of the patterns in dolphin language, and explicitly introduce these creatures to the components of human language. Realization of such an instrument may well border on the impossible, at least for many years to come.

The development of new instruments and techniques and the increased utilization of existing instruments are vital to the study of animal communication. Computers and television recording cameras should become commonplace in the scientific laboratory and in the field; sound tape recorders which can probe farther into the ultrasonic range must be designed and built; new instruments for the detection and analysis of odors must be forthcoming—and these should be able to transduce their findings to inked charts, just as the spectrograph does in recording sounds. We need to know (perhaps by means of some sort of highly sophisticated potentiometer) more about the mediation and integration of nerve impulses, particularly sensory ones—those having to do with the detection and interpretation of visual, acoustic, olfactory, and tactile stimuli.

Man's horizons are expanding in all directions, not alone on terra firma but beyond into the outer space of the ether and the inner space of the oceans as well. Increasingly man probes the life secrets of his fellow creatures—the secrets that help them to survive—for answers to imperative questions about how best to live with and benefit from the great challenges that lie ahead. In the new, exciting, and growing field of animal communication, the combined research of scientists in many disciplines promises to provide those answers at the same time it leads man to a better understanding of the animal world.

Selected Bibliography

Books

ALTMANN, STUART A. (ed.). *Social Communication Among Primates.* University of Chicago Press, Chicago, 1967.

ARMSTRONG, EDWARD A. *Bird Display and Behavior.* Oxford University Press, Inc., New York, 1947. General, nontechnical.

————. *A Study of Bird Song.* Oxford University Press, London, 1963. Technical.

BOURLIÈRE, FRANÇOIS. *The Natural History of Mammals.* Alfred A. Knopf, Inc., New York, 1954. Nontechnical, informative.

BROWN, VINSON. *How to Understand Animal Talk.* Little, Brown and Company, Boston, 1958. Especially suited to the juvenile reader.

BURTON, MAURICE. *Animal Courtship.* Frederick A. Praeger, Inc., New York, 1953. A popular general review.

CATHEY, J. D. *Animals and Their Ways.* Doubleday & Company, Inc., New York, 1965. Popular illustrated account for the general reader.

DARLING, FRANK. *A Herd of Red Deer.* Oxford University Press, London, 1937. Nontechnical; a classic.

DE VORE, IRVEN (ed.). *Primate Behavior.* Holt, Rinehart & Winston, Inc., New York, 1965. A series of technical reports by twenty-one authors; excellent chapter on communication by Peter Marler.

FRINGS, HUBERT and MABLE. *Animal Communication.* Blaisdell Publishing Company, New York, 1964. The authors assume that the reader has some knowledge of science, especially biology.

FRISCH, KARL VON. *Bees: Their Vision, Chemical Senses, and Language.* Cornell University Press, Ithaca, N.Y., 1950. Popular.

GRIFFIN, DONALD. *Listening in the Dark.* Yale University Press, New Haven, Conn., 1958. The acoustic orientation of bats and men; nontechnical.

HAYES, CATHERINE. *The Ape in Our House.* Harper & Brothers, New York, 1951. Popularized account.

HEINROTH, OSKAR and KATHARINA. *The Birds.* The University of Michigan Press, Ann Arbor, Mich., 1958. Popular, but much information useful to researchers.

HUXLEY, JULIA, and KOCH, LUDWIG. *Animal Language.* Grosset & Dunlap, Inc., New York, 1964. Popular. With record.

KELLOGG, WINTHROP N. *Porpoises and Sonar.* The University of Chicago Press, Chicago, 1961. Technical.

LANYON, W. E., and TAVOLGA, W. N. (eds.). *Animal Sounds and Communication.* Publication 7, American Institute of Biological Sciences, Washington, D.C., 1960. A series of technical reports by ten authors. With record.

Life Nature Library. Time, Inc., New York (recent publications). A series of popularized books about animals, birds, insects, mammals, primates, by various authors and the editors of *Life* magazine.

LILLY, JOHN C. *Man and Dolphin.* Doubleday & Company, Inc., New York, 1961. A popularized account of the biology and behavior of the bottle-nosed dolphin.

———. *The Mind of the Dolphin.* Doubleday & Company, Inc., New York, 1967. Nontechnical.

LINDAUER, MARTIN. *Communication Among Social Bees.* Harvard University Press, Cambridge, Mass., 1961. Nontechnical; a classic.

LORENZ, KONRAD Z. *King Solomon's Ring.* Thomas Y. Crowell Company, New York, 1952. An extremely witty account of animals and their behavior.

MILNE, LORUS and MARGERY. *The Senses of Animals and Men.* Atheneum Publishers, New York, 1962. Popular.

MORRIS, DESMOND and RAMONA. *Men and Apes.* McGraw-Hill Book Company, New York, 1966. Nontechnical.

PIERCE, GEORGE W. *The Songs of Insects.* Harvard University Press, Cambridge, Mass., 1948. Technical.

PORTMANN, ADOLF. *Animals as Social Beings.* The Viking Press, Inc., New York, 1961. Nontechnical.

SCHALLER, GEORGE B. *The Mountain Gorilla.* The University of Chicago Press, Chicago, 1963. A technical report of the ecology and behavior of the mountain gorilla.

————. *The Year of The Gorilla.* The University of Chicago Press, Chicago, 1964. A popularized account of the mountain gorilla.

SCOTT, JOHN PAUL. *Animal Behavior.* Anchor Books, Doubleday & Company, Inc., New York, 1963. Semitechnical; chapter on communication.

SLIJPER, E. J. *Whales.* Basic Books, Inc., Publishers, New York, 1962. Technical.

SOUTHWICK, CHARLES H. *Primate Social Behavior.* D. Van Nostrand Co., Inc., Princeton, N.J., 1963. A series of technical reports by seventeen authors.

TAVOLGA, W. N. *Marine Bio-acoustics* (2 vols.). Pergamon Press, Inc., New York, 1944. Technical.

TERRES, JOHN K. *Songbirds in Your Garden.* Thomas Y. Crowell Company, New York, 1953. A popularized account of the songbirds, with a special chapter on how to attract birds by means of sounds.

THORPE, W. H. *Bird-Song.* Cambridge University Press, Cambridge, England, and New York, 1961. Technical.

TINBERGEN, N. *Social Behavior in Animals.* Barnes & Noble, Inc., New York, 1967. A semipopular, generalized account.

————. *The Herring Gull's World.* Basic Books, Inc., Publishers, New York, 1961. Popular account. Also in paper (Doubleday & Company, Inc., New York).

WALKER, ERNEST P., and others. *Mammals of the World* (3 vols.). The Johns Hopkins Press, Baltimore, 1964. The definitive work on mammals.

WELLS, ROBERT. *Bionics*. Dodd, Mead & Co., New York, 1966. Popularized account for young adults of applying nature's techniques to machines.

WELTY, JOEL CARL. *The Life of Birds*. W. B. Saunders Co., Philadelphia, 1962. A textbook, concerned mainly with the biology of birds.

YOUNG, J. Z. *The Life of Mammals*. Oxford University Press, Inc., New York, 1957. A textbook of mammalian biology.

Recordings

Voices of the Night. Cornell University Records, Ithaca, N.Y. The calls of thirty-four frogs and toads of the United States and Canada.

American Bird Songs. Cornell University Records, Ithaca, N.Y. A collection of the songs of many of the birds of the northern and southern United States.

The Songs of Insects. Cornell University Records, Ithaca, N.Y. Calls of the common crickets, grasshoppers, and cicadas of the eastern United States.

Animal Language. Sounds Unlimited, Los Altos, Calif. Recordings of the voices of over three dozen terrestrial and aquatic animals, with narration by Vinson Brown. Especially suitable for juvenile listening.

Sounds of the American Southwest. Folkways Records & Service Corp., New York. Recorded sounds of birds, reptiles, amphibians, insects, and mammals of the region.

Sounds of Sea Animals. Folkways Records & Service Corp., New York. Recordings of representative underwater sounds produced by several species of fishes, invertebrates (such as snapping shrimp), sea cows, and porpoises.

Periodicals

Animal Kingdom. New York Zoological Society, New York Zoological Park, Bronx, N.Y. 10460. Nontechnical; well illustrated.

Audubon Magazine. National Audubon Society, 1130 Fifth Avenue, New York, N.Y. 10028. General; principally ornithology.

Canadian Field Naturalist. Ottawa Field-Naturalist Club, National Museum of Canada, Ottawa, Ontario, Canada. General articles on natural history.

Field and Stream. Holt, Rinehart & Winston, Inc., 383 Madison Avenue, New York, N.Y. 10017. Occasional popular articles on natural history.

Frontiers. The Academy of Natural Sciences, 19th Street and Parkway, Philadelphia, Pa. 19103. Nontechnical.

Natural History. The American Museum of Natural History. Central Park West at 79th Street, New York, N.Y. 10024. General; profusely illustrated.

Natural Wildlife. Natural Wildlife Foundation, 1412 16th Street, N.W., Washington, D.C. 20036. General, nontechnical.

Science. American Association for the Advancement of Science, 1515 Massachusetts Avenue, N.W., Washington, D.C. 20005. Excellent, authoritative articles reflecting recent investigations; technical.

Science Journal. Iliffe Industrial Publications, Ltd., Dorset House, Stamford Street, London, S.E. 1, England. Well-written occasional articles on life sciences; semitechnical.

Scientific American. 415 Madison Avenue, New York, N.Y. 10017. Well written and illustrated; semitechnical to technical.

Index

(For illustrations see list on pages viii and ix.)

alarm signals:
  of amphibians, 68–69
  of aquatic invertebrates, 18,
    25, 27
  of aquatic mammals, 126
  of birds, 73–75, 80–81
  of insects, 38–39, 41, 51, 52
  of land mammals, 106, 114–
    117
  of primates, 143, 144–145
  of reptiles, 60–61, 64
amphibians, 64–69
  alarm signals of, 68–69
  auditory signals of, 65–69
  chemical signals of, 70–72
  courtship of, 67–68
  ears of, 65–66
  visual signals of, 69–70
animal communication, *see*
    communication
ants:
  chemical signals of, 50–51
  tactile signals of, 43–46
ape family (*Pongidae*), 136
aquatic invertebrates, 13–18
  alarm signals of, 18, 25, 27
  auditory signals of, 13–14
  chemical signals of, 16–18

aquatic invertebrates (*cont.*)
  eyes of, 14, 22–23
  tactile signals of, 18
  visual signals of, 14–16
aquatic mammals, 119–133
  alarm signals of, 126
  auditory signals of, 123–130
  brain-mapping experiments
    with, 123
  courtship of, 122–123
  ears of, 123
  homing abilities of, 125
  olfactory signals of, 121–123
  parental care among, 122, 125
  tactile signals of, 121–123
  territorial defense of, 124
  visual signals of, 120–121
auditory signals:
  of amphibians, 65–69
  of aquatic invertebrates, 13–
    14
  of aquatic mammals, 123–130
  of bats, 114
  of bears, 111
  of bees, 38–41
  of birds, 77–89
  of chimpanzees, 141
  of coyotes, 113–114

auditory signals (*cont.*)
  of crickets, 37
  of crows, 84, 86
  of crustaceans, 14
  of dolphins, 128–130
  of fishes, 18–22
  of frogs, 65–69
  of geckos, 57
  of gorillas, 141–143, 148–150
  of grasshoppers, 37–38
  of *Gymnarchus niloticus*, 22
  of insects, 37–41
  of land mammals, 111–117
  of mollusks, 14
  of prairie dogs, 112
  of primates, 141–150
  of reptiles, 56–59
  of salamanders, 65–66
  of seals, 123–124
  of squirrels, 113
  variations in intensity of, 113
  of whales, 125–126

baboons, 139
  visual signals of, 151–152, 155, 156
badgers, 118
bats, 114
bears:
  auditory signals of, 111
  chemical signals of, 97
bees:
  auditory signals of, 38–41
  chemical signals of, 53–54
  sounds of, 34
  tactile signals of, 46–49
Betta splendens, 25
binoculars, 168
bioluminescence of insects, 42–43
birds, 73–94
  alarm signals of, 73–75, 80–81
  auditory signals of, 77–89
  courtship of, 80, 91–93
  ears of, 75, 77

birds (*cont.*)
  interspecific communication among, 81
  parental care among, 82–84
  songs of, 77–80
  syrinx of, 75
  territorial defense of, 86–87
  visual signals of, 89–93
brain mapping, 123
butterfles, 41

camera, 168
  magnetic-tape television, 170–171
cerebellum, 4
cerebral cortex, 4
cerebrum, 4
cetaceans, 119
chemical senses, 2
chemical signals:
  of amphibians, 70–72
  of ants, 50–51
  of aquatic invertebrates, 16–18
  of bears, 97
  of bees, 53–54
  of dogs, 98
  of fishes, 26–28
  of *Helix pomatia*, 18
  of insects, 49–54
  of land mammals, 96–99
  of moths, 53
  of primates, 139–140
  of prosimians, 139
  of reptiles, 63–64
  of skunks, 99
  of *Vorticella*, 18
chest beating, of primates, 141–143
chimpanzees:
  auditory signals of, 141
  visual signals of, 153, 155
cicadas, 30–32
coelenterates, 18

colors, of fishes, 23–25
communication:
  among animals, 10–12
  defined, 1–2
  interspecific:
    of badgers and coyotes, 118
    of birds, 81
    of land mammals, 117–118
    of primates, 157, 159
    of zebras, 117
  mechanisms and structures
    for, 3–4
  uses of, 6–8
compass, 168
courtship:
  of amphibians, 67–68
  of aquatic invertebrates, 15–
    16, 19–21
  of aquatic mammals, 122–123
  of birds, 80, 91–93
  of insects, 37, 38, 53
  of lagomorphs, 108
  of land mammals, 98, 99–100,
    102–103, 108–110, 115
  of reptiles, 62–63
coyotes:
  auditory signals of, 113–114
  communication with badgers
    by, 118
crickets, 37
crows, 84, 86
crustaceans:
  auditory signals of, 14
  visual signals of, 14–15

dogs:
  chemical signals of, 98
  visual signals of, 104
dolphins:
  auditory signals of, 128–130
  possibilities of talking with,
    132–133
  "sonar" of, 129, 130–131
domestic animals, 10

dominance hierarchy:
  in land mammals, 103–104
  in primates, 154–157
drumming, see chest beating

ears:
  of amphibians, 65–66
  of aquatic mammals, 123
  of birds, 75, 77
  of land mammals, 96
electric eels, 21–22
equipment:
  for ocean studies, 168
  for studying animals, 167–171
eyes:
  of aquatic invertebrates, 14,
    22–23
  of insects, 41–42

facial expressions:
  of land mammals, 103
  of primates, 151–153
fireflies, 42–43
fishes:
  auditory signals of, 18–22
  chemical signals of, 26–28
  colors of, 23–25
  tactile signals of, 26–28
  visual signals of, 22–26
flashlight, 168
friendliness:
  of land mammals, 102–103
  of primates, 140
frogs:
  auditory signals of, 65–69
  chorusing of, 66–67
  visual signals of, 69–70

geckos, 57
gorillas:
  auditory signals of, 141–143,
    148–150
  visual signals of, 152, 153, 156–
    157
grasshoppers, 37–38

grooming:
    of land mammals, 103
    of primates, 140
Gymnarchus, 11
Gymnarchus niloticus, 22

hearing, of insects (*see also*
    ears), 34–37
Helix pomatia, 18
herd animals, 106
homing, of aquatic mammals,
    125

insects, 29–54
    alarm signals of, 38–39, 41, 51,
        52
    auditory signals of, 37–41
    bioluminescence of, 42–43
    chemical signals of, 49–54
    courtship of, 37, 38, 53
    eyes of, 41–42
    hearing mechanisms of, 34–37
    ketones in, 51
    pheromones in, 49–54
    sound-producing mechanisms
        of, 30–34
    stridulation of, 30–32
    tactile signals of, 43–49
    visual signals of, 41–43
invertebrates, *see* aquatic in-
    vertebrates

ketones, 51

lagomorphs, 108
land mammals, 94–118
    alarm signals of, 106, 114–117
    auditory signals of, 111–117
    chemical signals of, 96–99
    courtship of, 98, 99–100, 102–
        103, 108–110, 115
    dominance hierarchy of, 103–
        104
    ears of, 96

land mammals (*cont.*)
    facial expressions of, 103
    grooming among, 103
    interspecific communication
        of, 117–118
    parental care among, 110, 116
    tactile signals of, 99–103
    territorial defense of, 97
    visual signals of, 103–111
languages, animal, 8–10
langurs, 155–156

mammals, *see* aquatic mam-
    mals; land mammals
mandrills, 151
mating, *see* courtship
methods for study, 161–171
mollusks, 14
monkeys:
    New World, 136, 138
    Old World, 136, 138–139
    proboscis, 151
    rhesus, 154–155
moths, 53

notebook, of investigator, 167–
    168

observation, in studying ani-
    mals, 162–165
Odontosyllis, 16
olfactory signals, of aquatic
    mammals, 121–123
opossums, 107
ossicles, Weberian, 21

parental care, 7–8
    among aquatic mammals, 122,
        125
    among birds, 82–84
    among land mammals, 110,
        116
    among primates, 135–136
pest control, 11

pheromones, 99
  in nonsocial insects, 52
  in social insects, 49–54
physical senses, 2
pinnepeds, 119
Pongidae, see ape family
porcupines, 107
porpoises, 128
prairie dogs:
  auditory signals of, 112
  visual signals of, 104, 106
primates, 135–159
  alarm signals of, 143, 144–145
  auditory signals of, 141–150
  chemical signals of, 139–140
  dominance hierarchy of, 154–157
  drumming (chest beating) of, 141–143
  facial expressions of, 151–153
  friendliness of, 140
  grooming among, 140
  interspecific communication of, 157, 159
  parental care among, 135–136
  tactile signals of, 140–141
  visual signals of, 151–157
  yawning by, 152, 153
prosimians, 136–138
  chemical signals of, 139

reproduction (*see also* courtship), 6–7
reptiles, 55–64
  alarm signals of, 60–61, 64
  auditory signals of, 56–59
  chemical signals of, 63–64
  courtship of, 62–63
  tactile signals of, 63–64
  visual signals of, 59–63

salamanders, 65–66
Sceptron pattern recognizer, 170
seals, 123–124

sense organs, 3–4
skunks:
  chemical signals of, 99
  visual signals of, 108
"sonar," dolphin, 129, 130–131
songs, of birds, 77–80
sounds:
  of insects, 30–34
  qualities of, 4
  reproduction of, 3–4
sound spectrograph, 168–170
sound vibrations, 3–4
species recognition, 6
spectrograph, sound, 168–170
squirrels, 113
stares, significance of, 104, 151
stridulation:
  of cicadas, 30–32
  of insects, 30–32
subordination, *see* dominance hierarchy
syrinx, of birds, 75

tactile signals:
  of ants, 43–46
  of aquatic invertebrates, 18
  of aquatic mammals, 121–123
  of bees, 46–49
  of coelenterates, 18
  of fishes, 26–28
  of insects, 43–49
  of land mammals, 99–103
  of primates, 140–141
  of reptiles, 63–64
tail, of primates, 153–154
tape recorder, variable-speed, 170
territorial defense, 6
  of aquatic mammals, 124
  of birds, 86–87
  of land mammals, 97
threats, of primates (*see also* alarm signals), 151
tools for study, 161–171
trophallaxis, 43–44

visual signals:
  of amphibians, 69–70
  of aquatic invertebrates, 14–
    16
  of aquatic mammals, 120–121
  of baboons, 151–152, 155, 156
  of *Betta splendens*, 25
  of birds, 89–93
  of butterflies, 41
  of chimpanzees, 153, 155
  of crustaceans, 14–15
  of dogs, 104
  of fireflies, 42–43
  of fishes, 22–26
  of frogs, 69–70
  of gorillas, 152, 153, 156–157
  of herd animals, 106
  of insects, 41–43
  of land mammals, 103–111
  of langurs, 155–156
  of mandrills, 151
  of *Odontosyllis*, 16
  of opossums, 107

visual signals (*cont.*)
  of porcupines, 107
  of prairie dogs, 104, 106
  of primates, 151–157
  of proboscis monkeys, 151
  of reptiles, 59–63
  of rhesus monkeys, 154–155
  of skunks, 108
  of wolves, 104
Vorticella, 18

warning signals, *see* alarm sig-
    nals
Weberian ossicles, 21
whales, 125–126
wildlife management, 11
wolves, 104

yawning, among primates, 152,
    153

zebra, interspecific communica-
    tion of, 117